Making a Difference at the Tar Creek Superfund Site

Community Efforts to Reduce Risk

Making a Difference at the Tar Creek Superfund Site
Community Efforts to Reduce Risk

Rebecca Jim and Marilyn Scott
Editors

LEAD Agency, Inc.
Vinita, Oklahoma

ISBN-13: 978-0-9797548-0-7
ISBN-10: 0-9797548-0-1

This publication was made possible by grant number R01 ES 08755 from the National Institute of Environmental Health Sciences (NIEHS). Its contents are solely the responsibility of the authors and do not necessarily represent the official views of the NIEHS, NIH.

Front cover photograph by Vaughn Wascovich. Used with permission.
Back cover photograph by Nancy Goldenberg. Used with permission.
Printed on 100% recycled paper.

Contents

Photo by Earl Dotter

Foreword

by Sheila Stogsdill
State Correspondent, *The Oklahoman*

The story of Tar Creek and its plight for justice might have been forgotten if it hadn't been for the mountain-sized chat piles that brought photographers and reporters from across the state and nation to northern Ottawa County. Tar Creek has been profiled in local and state newspapers for more than twenty years. *Time and Newsweek* magazines, as well as the *Washington Post* and the *New York Times* newspapers, even *Nightline*, have covered the EPA's top superfund site.

Photographers have shot endless photographs of the orange stained stones and ground covering that hugs the Tar Creek stream. Reporters have told stories of a mother discovering her child has learning disabilities and blaming herself for allowing the child to play near a chat pile or an elderly man plagued with multiple illnesses. Other times, reporters have informed the public how their tax dollars were being used or how a cleanup was halted by a federal investigation.

The citizens of Tar Creek have grown weary of twenty-seven years of promises by the county, state and federal government. As a reporter, I write about each new promise. Some governmental initiatives have been successful—others, not so much.

The first time I traveled down the main thoroughfare of Picher, behind the crumbling buildings and faded paint, I saw signs of a more prosperous time. Picher was on the route for presidential campaign stops. At one time, it was a booming community of more than 30,000 people. Old-timers told me those buildings were once dance halls full of music and laughter. They told me tales of playing baseball with Mickey Mantle or the thrill of seeing Bob Wills and the Texas Playboys who would ride into town by train once a month to entertain the miners and the town's people. The community hangs onto its pride with one hand but knowing they need to let go with the other hand for their own good.

As a reporter it's been my job to tell that story.

The sons and daughters of the mines
were raised on iron and lead.

A few may profit from the mines
but many pay the debt.
- Bill Honker

For our future generations
who will benefit from the work
that has been done.

Introduction

In the far northeastern corner of Oklahoma lies one of the worst toxic waste areas in the country: the Tar Creek Superfund Site, named after the creek that runs through it. This forty-seven-square-mile area in Ottawa County contains the six small towns of Picher, Cardin, Quapaw, Commerce, Miami and North Miami. It is also home to ten Indian tribes: the Quapaw, Seneca-Cayuga, Miami, Modoc, Wyandotte, Ottawa, Peoria, Shawnee, Eastern Shawnee, and Cherokee, who arrived in the area from many disparate places during the long years of upheaval and displacement after the arrival of European settlers. They were forced to leave their ancient lands and reestablish homes in this tall grassland prairie.

"Around the turn of the twentieth century, before Oklahoma became a state, lead and zinc were discovered here, and over 300 mines were opened in this forty-square-mile tract" (Kesson and Oyler 1999). Over the next five decades, hundreds of thousands of tons of lead, zinc and other minerals were extracted from it, providing raw materials for the majority of the American bullets of World Wars I & II, among other uses.

In the early days of the mines, this area was a boomtown, and the local economy flourished. By the early 1960s, however, mining activity had slowed considerably, and it had come to a halt by 1974. Since then, the area has struggled.

Abandoned mines honeycomb the entire area. When the mines were closed, the practices that had made them safe were also stopped. Pumps were shut down that had kept them free of water, and the pillars of earth that had kept the ground stable were allowed to be mined out. Most of the hundreds of mineshafts were not sealed, and surface and ground water slowly filled the underground caves and shafts as the aquifer refilled (Kesson and Oyler 1999). Oxygen, water and the exposed metals—high concentrations of zinc, lead, and cadmium—chemically reacted to produce sulphuric acid (Caron 2003). In 1979, this acid mine water began to discharge to the surface, contaminating the water in Tar Creek. It runs orange in many places and neon green where sewage flows into it. The fish left it long ago. "The more acidic the stream is, the less life it can support" (Caron 2003). The waters of the Roubidoux aquifer and Grand Lake are also at risk, and these are the major drinking water sources for a vast area.

Acres and acres of mine tailings, known as chat, dot the landscape. These chat piles, some of them two hundred feet high, are sources of lead poisoning through breathing the dust or it being carried by hands to mouths, which can cause cognitive disabilities, decreased growth, hyperactivity, and impaired hearing in children and high blood pressure and poor circulation in adults. These huge tailings are mostly unfenced and have been used for various forms of recreation and play over the years. The contamination has had dire effects on the health of people, animals, plant life, and soil of the area, much of it accumulating slowly over time so it was practically invisible.

Health concerns are a major issue in Ottawa County. The cancer rates for the area are remarkably higher than the rest of the state, and the state is higher than the rest of the nation (Kesson and Oyler 1999). The little town of Miami even has two of its own dialysis units.

In 1983, the area was given its Superfund designation due to the severe and pervasive pollution of water, soil, and air. A first study was done by the EPA, in which the primary focus was the water itself. This resulted in the implementation of what was called Operable Unit 1 (OU1), to address the acid mine water flowing into Tar Creek from the mines and the need to plug wells to protect the Roubidoux aquifer. The remedy was not effective. The mine water still flows onto the surface and into Tar Creek. But there was no immediate followup, and the area and its worsening situation seemed to be abandoned.

Around that same time, the U.S. Representative from Oklahoma, Mike Synar, initiated a task force hearing, demonstrating his personal concern about the state's environmental situation. When the Cherokee Volunteer Society was formed, its Tar Creek project was dedicated to him, and the Mike Synar Environmental Award has been given to worthy individuals yearly since 1997.

There was little public awareness of the seriousness of the situation until the early 1990s, when a staff member at the Indian Health Service noticed that the blood lead levels of a number of local children were abnormally high. That started a ripple of concern. But where does one start? And who does what? How does a community grab hold and grapple with solutions when the problems are so overwhelming and interlinked?

In the next pages, the answers to those questions unfold, told by some of the many people who have been involved in the process from their individual perspectives and involvement. Things did begin to change, and a remarkable and extremely important success has been achieved: The number of young children, six years and under, who are at highest risk of the profound and long-lasting effects of lead poisoning has been reduced from close to half of the population to very few (the percentages mentioned by various people vary according to different measurements, but the overall result is consistent).

Two major components of this turn-around came from outside the area, a grant-funded project named TEAL and an EPA residential soil cleanup; they began at roughly the same time. Both of them rested on the strong foundation of two community groups, The Cherokee Volunteer Society and LEAD Agency, both active in heightening awareness of Tar Creek's situation and passionately engaged in enlisting help to change it. TEAL's work included the local community, as people's stories show, and a number of other complementary efforts and actions contributed to the total outcome.

Events did not follow one another in a straight line and so the telling of them doesn't either. We begin with Coweta Ulrey's reminiscences of how things were in early days and then present Dr. David Bellinger's explanation of the effects of lead poisoning and his involvement with Tar Creek. From there, people's stories follow one another in a rough approximation of chronology and area, but please keep in mind that major efforts occurred simultaneously. The narratives then continue into speculation and planning of the next steps in this living process.

We hope you find it a terrific and inspiring story. And this is just the first chapter of Tar Creek Superfund Site's return to a state of true health. We hope to tell the subsequent chapters soon.

Acknowledgments

We acknowledge the contributions of Jennifer Caron, a graduate of California Technical Institute in Pasadena, California. She was a Quaker Witness at Tar Creek for the summer of 2001. She has researched Tar Creek's history extensively; been an eloquent spokesperson, interesting others in the work; and continues her own involvement whenever and however possible. We thank her wholeheartedly for her help. We also thank Earl Hatley, Dana Jim and Judith David for their eagle eyes and excellent suggestions and the Wyandotte Nation for their generous support.

To give some background, brief descriptions of TEAL and the EPA's soil cleanup as well as several maps follow to help orient you.

TEAL—Tribal Efforts Against Lead

Through a NIEHS initiative establishing community-based participatory research (CBPR), the TEAL Project was funded from 1996 to 2006. CBPR grants brought scientists and community members together to conduct research on the effects of environmental health hazards and to educate local residents on how to avoid or mitigate their risk of exposure. Community members participated throughout the project—with the research, intervention effort and design implementation and dissemination.

The University of Oklahoma received the 1996 grant for a project on environmental lead exposures of Native American children in northeast Oklahoma. Through the project, culturally appropriate materials and approaches were developed. Lay health advisors from each of the eight tribes were taught to deliver lead prevention messages to friends and family and more broadly to the whole community.

Blood screenings were done in 1997, 2000, and 2004. In the final screening two individuals involved did not respect the research process and as a result, the specific impact of TEAL and related activities on the prevalence of elevated blood lead levels in area children could not be assessed using accepted research methods.

TEAL has also made this book and film possible, detailing much of the tribal efforts against lead and the other efforts going on at the same time.

EPA Residential Soil Cleanup at the Tar Creek Superfund Site

Data provided to EPA by the Indian Health Services in the early 1990s showed that an alarming number of children in the Tar Creek Site area had elevated blood lead levels. As a result, EPA evaluated and sampled approximately 3,350 residential properties in the Tar Creek Superfund Site to determine if elevated levels of lead were located on any part of these properties.

Of these properties, approximately 2,330, or about 69%, were cleaned up by EPA. The remaining 31% of the evaluated and sampled properties were either below the action level of 500 parts per million for lead or the property owner denied access.

Between 1995 and 2007, EPA remediated 2,330 properties, including 145 in Cardin, 781 in Commerce, 12 in Miami, 179 in North Miami, 795 in Picher, 415 in Quapaw, and 3 at various locations elsewhere in Ottawa County. These include 5 daycare centers, 12 schools, and 19 parks. The remediation of the yards and public areas and the educational outreach programs implemented by the Ottawa County Health Department has had a significant impact on children's health.

Location of the Picher mining district

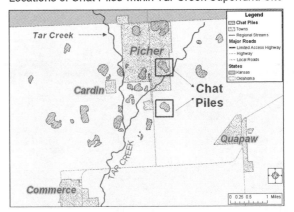

Grand Lake Watershed with Tribal Treaty Boundaries

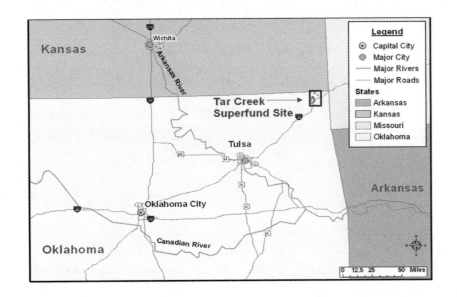

Locations of Chat Piles within Tar Creek Superfund Site

Coweta Ulrey
Clanmother
I have a burden for my Indian people.

I live in Quapaw, Oklahoma. I am a member of the Ottawa Tribe of Oklahoma. I was a Dawes, and at one time my brother, now deceased, was the Chief of our tribe. I was secretary/treasurer of the Ottawa Tribe at one time. I belonged to the United States cadet nurse corps in World War II.

I have a burden for my Indian people. I mean Indian people. When I was young, there were no tribes mentioned. We were all Indians. When we went to school, it was just Indians. You didn't belong to this tribe or that tribe. Our parents were the same way. They were just Indians. It was much different than it is now. But I do have that burden, especially for children. I have always loved children.

I did work at the Quapaw school, and there were children in one family I worried about. They did have trouble learning. Some were in special education, some in L.D. or learning disability classes. It is something that you feel. You want to do something when you see a whole family of children who need help. There has to be something wrong.

The principal and I had visited the home in Picher. It just bothered me when four or five in one family needed help. They were a poor family. The house had no screens on the windows or door. I am sure that the lead had something to do with the whole family. I was interested in the lead be-

cause of these children. It should have been discovered way before it was. Those children won't be able to work or hold down jobs. It is sad. I think it was great that they started to check blood lead levels. I think they should still check children when they are really young, as well as when they get older. I am still concerned about it.

It is like everything else. We don't do things when we should. I know and appreciate what Rebecca Jim has done with Harvard University. They are interested because somebody has to be. We don't want other children to go through that.

Our environment is not anything like it used to be. When I was young, we had beautiful water in our rivers and our creeks but not anymore. That is sad. That is the biggest change I have seen in my lifetime. I hate to have these children grow up in a polluted environment like this.

My dad passed away in 1947, but when he was alive, we had a mine on our land. He capped that himself with a big concrete slab. Other people should have done that too. Eagle-Picher left a mess for the rest of us to clean up.

There are still people who don't believe there is a problem because they don't know anybody who died of lead poisoning. We didn't know anyone who died of cancer either, but evidently they had these things. Back in those days, many health problems like cancer were not diagnosed, that is what I say.

I still like the old ways.
I like the way when we were Indians.

David Bellinger PhD
Professor of Neurology
Harvard Medical School

Lead poisoning is my prime area of interest, and I'd like to give you a general understanding of its occurrence in children. Lead poisoning is considered to be the most common form of chemical intoxication in children. Measuring the concentration of lead in the blood is the way in which a child's level of risk is most often determined. The level is expressed as the number of micrograms (µg) of lead per deciliter (dL or 100 ml) of whole blood. The level of lead in blood that is considered to be "too much" has dropped dramatically over the past thirty-five years. In the 1960s a level of 70 µg/dL was considered to be the upper limit of normal. This level was reduced to 40 in 1971, 30 in 1978, 25 in 1985, and 10 in 1991. Some public health advocates are currently urging the U.S. Centers for Disease Control to reduce it to 5 or even 2 µg/dL, although as of 2007, the Centers have no plan to do so.

Fortunately, the exposure of the general population of U.S. children to lead has also declined dramatically in recent decades as a result of such measures as the elimination of lead from residential paint, solder, and gasoline. Whereas eighty-eight percent of preschool children had blood lead levels greater than 10 µg/dL in the late 1970's, and the average level was about 15 µg/dL. The average is currently below 2 µg/dL, and fewer than two percent of children have a level greater than 10 µg/dL. Although this represents a tremendous public health success, two % of U.S. children is still a large number, which translates to several hundred thousand children. We must be careful in how we think about what a normal or acceptable blood lead level is. A blood lead level of 10 µg/dL should not be viewed as safe because recent research increasingly shows adverse effects occurring below this level, with no indication that there is a threshold level below which these adverse effects do not occur. We must conclude that excessive lead exposure remains a problem in this country. Moreover, certain disparities persist, with the blood lead levels remaining relatively higher among children who are poor or members of minority groups.

Lead harms children in many ways. Lead poisoning can be fatal (at levels above about 150 µg/dL), although fortunately deaths are now rare. At lower levels, it affects many organ systems in the body, including the kidneys, the blood, the immune system, the thyroid, and, perhaps most important, the nervous system. In children, it is the adverse effects on the developing central nervous system, (*i.e.*, the brain and spinal cord) that are of greatest concern. In adults, the effects on the nervous system tend to be seen more in the peripheral nervous system (*i.e.*, the nerves in the areas of the body other than the brain and spinal cord). In children higher lead exposures are associated with lower intelligence and problems in motor development, attention, organization skills, and academic skills such as reading and math. These problems appear to be long-lasting, as some research shows that the effects continue into adulthood. If a child's lead exposure becomes very high, drugs are sometimes used to help the child's body excrete the lead, but studies indicate that these drugs do not prevent the learning and behavioral problems from occurring, nor does it reverse them. The lesson from this research is that if we wish to prevent lead from harming children, we must prevent them from being exposed in the first place because we have few treatment options later.

Because we know how lead can harm a child's development, the fact that the percentage of children in the Tar Creek region with a blood lead level greater than 10 µg/dL decreased from forty-two percent to four percent (42% to 4%) in recent years is enormously important. The children's futures will be brighter than they otherwise would have been had efforts not been taken to prevent their continued exposure to lead. Nevertheless, because, as noted above, we should not regard 10 µg/dL as a safe level, efforts do need to continue to further reduce this percentage.

> If we wish to prevent lead from harming children, we must prevent them from being exposed in the first place.

Our Work in Ottawa County

Because the mine tailings (chat) in the Tar Creek area contains different metals that, at sufficiently high levels, can affect children's neurodevelopment, we obtained funding from the Milton Fund of Harvard University to conduct a small pilot study, to determine whether these metals, either individually or in combination, are associated with children's intelligence, learning, memory, academic skills, and behavior. In 2004 we recruited a group of thirty-two fifth and sixth graders from two science classrooms in the Miami schools to participate in the study.

Each child was administered a battery of tests lasting two hours, and each contributed a sample of hair, which we analyzed for arsenic, manganese, cadmium, and lead. We could not draw any conclusions about whether the levels of metals in the hair of these children were low or high because no nationally representative information is available for comparison. We did, however, find that children with higher levels of arsenic and manganese tended to have lower scores on the tests of verbal intelligence, verbal learning, and verbal memory, but not on the other tests administered. (Higher levels of cadmium and lead in hair were not associated with scores on any of the tests.)

Strikingly, it was the children who had higher levels of both arsenic and manganese that were largely responsible for these findings. Children who had a higher level of arsenic or manganese, but not both, tended to perform as well as other children. This finding is important because it suggested that the usual practice of focusing on one pollutant at a time might be misleading. In the "real world," we are exposed to mixtures of pollutants, and so in our studies we need to take this complexity into account. We are doing so in our current work in Ottawa County, which focuses on following a large group of children from birth to five years of age. In this study, we are measuring the children's exposures to several metals at various times in their early years. The findings of our pilot study were published in the journal *Neurotoxicology* in 2006.

After conducting the research and learning the results, I returned to Miami in 2005 and met with many of the students who had participated in the study. They had been an exceptionally wonderful group of children to work with. They were cooperative, pleasant and extremely patient with what must have seemed to them to be silly tasks. For example, they were asked to remember a shopping list or copy strange patterns of lines.

I was amazed to see that although it had only been a year since I had seen them as part of the study, they had grown from children into adolescents. I was deeply affected by our meeting because some of them asked whether they were "retarded" because of having grown up in the Miami area. They mentioned being teased by children from other towns who were aware of the pollution problems in Miami.

I tried to reassure them that their scores were solidly in the normal range, and that while we did see associations between higher arsenic and manganese levels and scores on certain verbal tests, we did not know whether the levels of arsenic and manganese that they had were any higher than those of other children in the U.S.

Photo courtesy LEAD Agency, Inc. archives

Dr. David Bellinger and Rebecca Jim are surrounded by sixth grade science students at Will Rogers Middle School.

Rita Frayser
Social Worker
Ottawa County Department
of Human Services
Parent

In the very early days, there did not seem to be much awareness about what lead did to children. The first thing that alerted me was many of my clients lived in old houses with lead-based paint. I encouraged my clients to get their children checked for lead since young children chew on things.

A couple of my clients asked one of the local doctors about checking for lead and were told that it was not a problem. During their yearly physical, lead testing would have been covered in the cost. I don't think I had a single one succeed in getting the doctor to do the test. I always thought the doctor just didn't want to be bothered. It was very frustrating.

As we began to understand what was happening in Picher because of the contaminated chat, more information became available about what heavy metals did to children. Before this time, people were completely unaware of the dangers.

A new playground was installed at Alexander Elementary School in Commerce, and chat was actually put on the playground when my own children were in school there. I have

I think students made a difference. They should be proud of that.

always wondered just how much direct exposure the children received by playing there, as well as how much the exposure to the contaminated dust affected them.

Most of my older son's health problems are hereditary. But I have wondered whether any of my younger son's learning disabilities or memory problems were caused by his exposure to lead at a young age. He was at that school from kindergarten on. I have never been completely convinced that there were no health effects from that exposure.

I have always been concerned about the behavior of some of the other children in the area, especially those living in Picher. Some of the children in my son's day care were extremely aggressive. I have wondered what effect the exposure had on their behavior. Since they were never tested, there is no way of knowing.

There has been a huge reversal in attitude among many people. I think it all started with the Cherokee Volunteers and the high school Tar Creek Project. No one else was interested. No one else wanted to hear about it. I think it was the high school group that made the difference.

I remember the Tar Creek tours and the student involvement. Some of the children were very enthusiastic about their research and taking water samples. They spent a lot of time looking up the various metals, and I was amazed at how concerned the children were. They were extremely interested, even as long as fifteen years ago.

The changes have been tremendous. The Indian tribes were not interested in doing anything at all. Now they are more than on the bandwagon; they are leading the parade.

Debi Wesley RN, PHN
Public Health Nurse
Northeast Tribal Health Center
(formerly Indian Clinic)
Parent

I don't know when to relax until they say there is no evidence of lead.

The cool thing about my job is that it is so versatile. There is never enough of me to get around like I want. It is always exciting.

When I started here fifteen years ago, there were thirty-six employees. Now we have sixty-nine, and I am still the only public health nurse. With the population we have, there should be three of me to do the work. It's just me, and I work really hard: 1 for 5000 served.

When I walked in this door fifteen years ago, the very first person to come visit me was Dr. Elaine Mader, and she came in with results. She had been testing kids for lead, and she said, "I don't know what to do with this, but this is a problem. We need to address this." That's when I got on the line with Centers for Disease Control (CDC) and started learning about lead. I learned a lot really quick, and we got our policies in order for the testing.

The next thing we did was get our sanitarian Don Ackerman involved. He helped with the home inspections. One day a week, I was in charge of immunizations, seeing twenty-five to thirty kids, with standing orders to do lead levels as well. We did some mass education concerning nutrition, and then, thank goodness, the county health program started up. Then the TEAL Project came along soon after.

When we started fifteen years ago, we were seeing horrendous numbers. We are not finding what they call truly elevated lead levels now. We don't see levels above ten anymore. But we are seeing sixes and sevens, and I am still concerned about those. At one time I was happy when I saw a six or seven. Now when we see those numbers, we talk to the parents about it. We educate them on nutrition and diet and then refer them to the Ottawa County lead education program with Susan Waldron. Now we see a lot of threes. The more low numbers, the better we feel. We even find a few negatives.

Lessons Learned....

The more you read about lead poisoning, the scarier it is. I had children myself and had just moved here to this area. At that time Danny was ten and Molly was six months old.

My approach with my own children was basic. It is like seat belts; there is not an option. You get in the car; you wear your seatbelt. When you come into the house, you wash your hands and take off your shoes. Teach the children, and they will continue it.

It is not natural to have lead in your blood.

Shirley Chesnut DO
Indian Clinic
Grand Lake Mental Health
Parent

Unacknowledged problems are never going to be solved.

I worked as a physician at the Indian Clinic, and I noticed that there was an increase of kids coming in from the Picher school system with a diagnosis of ADHD. I told one of the nurses. We had so many kids coming in for Adderall and Ritalin. There were more from Picher than there were from Miami, and Picher is much smaller. I didn't think it should be that way. I was wondering out loud with one of the nurses about the possibility of overdiagnosing. We also wondered whether or not the teachers were expecting a behavior level from kids that they weren't capable of at that point.

One of the nurses standing there had grown up in that area, and she said, "Well, it's probably the lead they are exposed to because if you look up the symptoms for high lead levels, they are almost exactly the same as the symptoms you see with ADD and ADHD. Maybe that's why so many of the kids from Picher are coming in needing these prescriptions. It looks like they have all these learning disabilities and ADHD and difficulty concentrating and trouble reading and on and on." So I looked up the symptoms and it's true. There was a huge overlap between ADHD symptoms and elevated lead levels. So I said, "As long as we have the kids here, let's go ahead and get the lead level blood work because we are already getting hemoglobins on those kids anyway." So we did.

The kids who had ADHD symptoms were coming back with lots of high lead levels. I didn't do any formal analysis of the percentage. I do remember that it was remarkably high, and so we let the public health nurse know. She talked to Don Ackerman who worked in environmental health. After that, he started looking into it. The two of them got their heads together and did some even bigger samples, and we found out that the problem was even bigger than we had realized.

I brought my own children in to be tested because they grew up in this area. Out of my four children, three came back with high lead levels. They weren't actionable at that time. The acceptable range was much higher than it is now. So I'm not sure that all four of them wouldn't have come back positive with the levels they use now. But the highest level was the child I had been told looked like he had ADHD. The baby had the lowest level. I assume that was because she hadn't played outside, getting any of the chat dust on her hands. I think that the reason that my boys came back with higher levels was because they did play outside a lot, and a lot of the alley ways and even playgrounds in Miami were covered with chat. It was a little bit scary because I didn't really know what to do at that time.

It is always frightening to find out you live in an area where it's dangerous to your children's health. It can even affect their potential IQ. Every parent would worry about that. But what would the solution be? Move the whole city? So it was a little bit frightening as this information came out in Northeast Oklahoma. It was devastating to learn that our home would be viewed as an undesirable place to live or for businesses to come or for anyone who wanted to raise a family to be. Who would want to be where your child's IQ is going to be affected by the environment?

This will always be our home. I remember my son Mark said, "Mom, Tar Creek is my backyard, and that's where we like to go to play. This is where I was born." It meant a lot to him to try to find out what was going on and see what could be done about it. When Mark was about ten, I remember he went from yard to yard in our neighborhood taking samples of the soil. He took Ziploc baggies and plastic spoons. He'd dig up a portion of dirt out of a person's yard and then drop it with the spoon in the bag in case it was contaminated, zip it up, and put a label on it indicating whose yard it was from. He got samples from all his friends' yards where they played to see whose yard might be contaminated and whose yard wasn't.

The house in our neighborhood that had stucco walls, Spanish style, had the highest. It was an old home built in the 1920s. They had used chat in the stucco to make it bumpy, to add texture. It was built by one of Miami's five original families. The rocks and the mining had made them wealthy.

Rebecca Jim took Mark's samples to the EPA headquarters and asked them to test them. They could have said, "No, we're not doing that." But they did test the samples, and then they gave us the results. That one yard was the worst because they had just redone that stucco and the old stucco had sat out in the yard.

I remember when Laura would wash her hands, she would sing, "One scrubby bear, two scrubby bears," and she couldn't stop washing until she got to ten scrubby bears. Laura still has her little nailbrush with the BEE.

My son Matt has a very intelligent friend who often mentions things about his Tar Creek connection. His Picher/Tar Creek experience had a huge impact on him. Think about what it would be like to find out, now that you are a young adult—sixteen to seventeen years old—that you had high blood lead levels as a child, and you realize that it can result in a lower IQ. You also find out that you might have some learning disabilities and not be able to comprehend things as fast as you would have otherwise. It would be difficult to cope with at that age. I can't imagine, because at that age you think everything is wrong with you anyway. He talks about it and makes jokes about it, which makes me know he's thought about it a lot.

At low levels the effects are so subtle that a person wouldn't necessarily notice. However, the impact could be far-reaching. It might involve the ability to make judgments, to make accurate assessments of the world around you, and to be able to be in control of your emotions—to be able to sit still, to be able to concentrate long enough to learn to read or to learn to read well. You might learn to read but not really well and comprehend what you are reading.

We know that we've lowered lead levels, but we also know that we have a generation of kids who grew up with high levels. Dr. David Bellinger's work and Dr. Bruce Lampier's work shows that a reading of ten is too high. When we did the original work, twenty was the level to worry about. We were only cautious with readings of fifteen to ten. On home visits, we told parents not to worry about blood lead levels of ten or below. At that time we were told not to worry unless the reading was above twenty. My children's blood lead levels were seventeen, thirteen, twelve, and seven.

My husband's family was born and raised in this area. His grandfather settled here. When it all first started, I looked at him and said, "We need to move. We have four kids. We need to move!" He said, "You know I've worked for the past fifteen years to establish a law practice here. I can't just leave, just pick up and start a law practice somewhere else. Shirley, that would be too hard. We can't leave."

The next best thing I figured was to find out where my kids were getting contaminated. The house is just several hundred feet from Quail Creek, and boys being boys, they loved to get down around the creek and look for frogs, snakes and that sort of stuff. They were down there a lot. I think that's where it was. At home I made sure that my kids got lots of iron and calcium.

Unacknowledged problems are never going to be solved. I felt like it doesn't really matter what it does to us as a community initially economically because we can't just sweep this under the rug. There is no way to hide the problem. The impact is too devastating.

So I am really proud of how our community has responded to it because historically there were a lot of people who lived here that were very proud of the fact that their grandfathers and great-grandfathers had been miners. So it was hard for them to deal with the fact that the mining has caused such a great environmental impact on the community. As time went by, some of those people turned out to be some of the strongest supporters of the efforts to address the problem.

Note: Shirley's youngest child Laura accompanied her to test sinkhole water where children swim. As an eighth grader, she wrote the poem following her quote.

This is where we are from. This is my home. We might as well try to prevent things from happening and make people more aware of what's already happened.
--Laura Chesnut

Here it's dangerous
Sinkholes and chat piles galore
So close to my home
--Laura Chesnut

I came to be the Indian Counselor at the junior high school in Miami the year before Tar Creek turned orange. When that happened, since it was in the news, everyone expected it would be fixed— especially after Tar Creek got its infamous Superfund rating. I went to Mike Synar's task force hearing and took my son, who was nine years old at the time (he's now a lawyer). We both took notes—his were better than mine with little maps he had drawn. I kept them.

Dr. John Neuberger showed a picture of a chat pile and was very concerned about it. Everyone in the room saw only a chat pile. He used a pointer to show what worried him. It was very simple—the footprints made by a child who had walked there.

That made a big impression on me.

Photo courtesy TEAL archives

Rebecca Jim
Clanmother
Cherokee Volunteer Society Sponsor
LEAD Agency Executive Director

Nobody talked about Tar Creek much when EPA left us, and no one talked about the mountains of mine waste we call chat.

Since then, it seems to me that I've just been in a position to say Yes to opportunities that have come along and to appreciate questions. Nancy Scott, of the Cherokee Nation, was looking for someone to take on a Service Learning project. That was the start of the Cherokee Volunteer Society, and those kids have done some awesome, powerful things. Their interest in making a difference in their community grew from cultural awareness to the awareness of the environment, and then its health impacts. The Tar Creek Project began when two new students, Chris and Season, asked, what other environmental problems did we have. A great deal came from their question. Students swinging into action year after year. The Cherokee Volunteers would not be stopped. From Kent Curtis, John Micka and John Mott they received the background they needed to really get started.

They wanted to have a Fish Tournament on Tar Creek, but without fish? Yes. They would have an awareness event every year and call it a Fish Tournament and keep doing it until there were fish again in that creek. They researched and wrote poetry, inspiring all of us with their efforts in two anthologies that were published by the Cherokee Nation, the first and edited by Nancy Scott and the second by Marilyn Scott.

There was a time when their parents could swim and fish in Tar Creek.

The Cherokee Volunteers' service learning project allowed Miami High School to become one of the nation's Leader Schools. Many of our students got to attend national conferences and present about their project. Those experiences inspired them to want to host their own national conference right here about Tar Creek.

Another initiative that service learning encouraged was more student voice. When Wanis Euran heard what we were doing and why, he was so moved, he just jumped up and said, *"WE OUGHT TO CALL THE NEW YORK TIMES!"* I had to agree and told him he should. And he did. They sent a reporter and a photographer and stayed four days.

At the public library there was a repository of all the documents EPA had generated over the years about Tar Creek. Several community members would meet together and read sections and take notes and list questions that we still had.

I transferred colleges to keep from having to take speech. Even asking questions out loud in a classroom was always hard. So the answer was to sit on the front row at meetings and ask from there. Or write a question down and pass it to the next person for them to ask. There were so many questions and answers we all needed.

After attending an EPA meeting, one of my students asked if her exposures as a child might have had some effect on her as a teenager. She went on to say that she had a chat pile in her backyard, but also that her dad had built her a sandbox and filled it with that fine sand that we now know was very high in lead. I had to try to find out. Finding that answer took awhile, and took asking more questions myself.

During that summer I found a tiny mention of research Rokho Kim had done on exposure to lead between ages seven and twenty. So I called information and actually got him on the phone. He was very helpful and explained that we could find out about that student's exposure as a child by testing a tooth, a baby tooth, since it was like a time capsule of exposure. He agreed to test other teeth, too, and would serve as our "Tooth Fairy."

We collected teeth from children, adults, and the baby tooth of the student who had wondered about her childhood exposure. When calling that number back for the results, the two people who answered, Dr. Robert Wright and Dr. Howard Hu, have stayed committed to our community. A long-term relationship with the Harvard School of Public Health ultimately resulted in the NIH Children's Center, a seven million dollar research project on the multiple metals exposures occurring here on our children. This project is now led by Dr. Joe Brain who sees Tar Creek as a poster child of the environmental and health consequences of mining.

At another EPA meeting George Mayer stood up and told the story about his horses. The acid mine water stained his horses legs and feet, and though he knew about stains from the brick business, he couldn't get those out. He said, "I have asked the EPA, the DEQ, the Bureau of Mines to fix the bore holes on my property. Isn't there anybody out there that will do something about my land?"

The next day after work I went to see George Mayer. He had a real estate office just around the corner from Miami High School. I told him I wasn't really sure what we could do, but we would organize and we would do something about his land. He had told me many times about his horses and how it broke his heart to sell them.

There were many things that the Cherokee Volunteer Society could do, but as a school-based group there were also some limitations, so a group of us adults gathered to form a non-profit. I called Earl Hatley to advise us as he had the Cherokee Volunteer Society years before. We still had no name. The name emerged from a small meeting that resulted in the HUD lead-based paint grant. The question around the table was, who would be the *lead agency* to take on that big grant. I said we won't do that, it is too much, but our little organization will take that name. "We'll be the LEAD Agency." Then we had to determine what each letter would stand for. L for *local,* E for *environmental,* A for *action,* of course. It was easy until we got to the D. *Demanded* never really seemed right, but I guess we have been demanding— just not in the way most would imagine.

It took us three years to go ahead and apply for IRS status. It was a big step, and we did it in order to qualify for the technical assistance grant from EPA. We hired Gary Lawley to read through all of those EPA documents and sum them up for regular folks to understand.

NO MORE TAR CREEKS and no more mining. If they can't clean up our site, they won't clean up the next one. Tribes are targets and need to take note.

When TEAL had started up, I served on the Community Advisory Board (CAB), but wanted to be one of the clanmothers, too. That was quite an experience. I really had never been much of a joiner, but that was a group of people that came together and worked to actively protect children. It was such a responsibility to take on.

We saved IQ points. Someday they may be able to figure out how many. We know that children's lead levels came down because of the prevention methods that were taught to parents, teachers, and to children themselves and because of the remedial work done by EPA. Which one did more? We will never really know. Was spending all that money worth it? If it saved one IQ point, it was. You can't buy them back once they are gone.

The second round of TEAL involved working with youth at the Picher and Quapaw schools. I already knew that youth could do remarkable work from the efforts by the Cherokee Volunteers. I had retired from my job as a school counselor so it was fun to work with Kristen Thomas and take part in these projects with youth and the clanmothers and fathers.

Churches have written resolutions about Tar Creek, starting with the United Methodists, then the Episcopal, the United Churches of Christ and the Quakers. EPA had never heard of that happening at any other site.

Sally Whitecrow came up with the idea of the clanmothers. I never knew it would touch our lives and empower us so much.

Our children keep telling these messages, like Ben Temple, that a creek is a terrible thing to waste. Children have been able to share their pictures and messages of hope. But the photographers and journalists keep coming and the images keep showing that there is more to do.

Remembering....

Through the years I have given lots of Toxic Tours. Once while standing on that bridge where Tar Creek mixes with the acid mine water, I got the opportunity to meet Robert Kennedy, Jr. I actually had the nerve to ask him about having a Riverkeeper program for Tar Creek and the watershed. We had been working on it, but that afternoon, we got the word we would be approved. LEAD Agency has the 117th with Earl Hatley being the GRAND Riverkeeper!

One other time, while standing with Miami High School students on that bridge, all looking down at that water, I asked Ryan Lowell, a sophomore at the time, what he saw. He didn't even pause. He just said he saw, "An eternal flow of evil." Well, that about summed it up for the day, for sure.

A seventh grade Indian student once said, "We're Indians, we ought to be for the environment." That statement has always stayed in my head. Years after he was out of high school, he had taken his four-wheeler over to the chat piles. He showed us the ticket he received when he got caught. One of the sheriffs worked really hard to help get the message out that the piles were hazardous. Anyone caught crossing the ditch would be destroying county property and subject to ticketing. He got the first ticket given.

Gary Lawley, PhD
LEAD Agency Technical Advisor

How could this, the first and largest of EPA Superfund Sites, be so neglected?

I am an environmental scientist with considerable experience at EPA Superfund Sites. Several years ago, I was on vacation in my home town in Oklahoma and read an article in the newspaper about children in Cardin and Picher having extremely high levels of lead in their blood from the lead mines, which had been designated as the Tar Creek Superfund Site. My immediate thought was, "How could this happen?" The hazards of lead were well known, even to the miners before the mines were abandoned. EPA has prevented problems with lead at dozens of Superfund Sites for years. I decided to get involved. I went to the site and was immediately impressed and dismayed. What a mess!

I contacted the Quapaw Environmental Department, and they arranged for me to meet with the Quapaw Tribal Leaders and with the LEAD Agency. LEAD Agency had just received a Technical Adviser grant. I submitted a proposal, and my proposal was selected. Consequently, I began working directly with local citizens. Then, and since, I have continually been disappointed in the low priority this site has received by the Oklahoma resource agencies and state government, the EPA and the Army Corps of Engineers.

Basically, there have been three work efforts, at Tar Creek.

EPA calls each work effort an operable unit (OU), and they number each. OU1 was poorly planned, underfunded and accomplished little. OU2 was done in response to local citizens finding high levels of lead in their children's blood. Progress has been made in this area. OU3 was in response to a local group finding hazardous wastes stored at Tar Creek that were an imminent hazard to the public.

Why hadn't the EPA or other state agencies found and eliminated these problems? Well, they simply never looked very hard (conducted a holistic evaluation of this site), found the problems, or set priorities for protecting the people and the environment. One reason for this was their failure to establish a responsible party with the money to remediate the site, and EPA has consistently refused to apply much of their own funds or effort to this site.

EPA's proposed OU4 left me again dismayed. This approach puts most of the onus for clean up on the parties that have scattered lead-contaminated chat at hundreds of locations. Much of this chat wound up in school yards and other public locations. Also, EPA now wants the agencies that have been unable or unwilling to oversee chat dispersal in the past to oversee the work. EPA did not involve the public in the important decisions regarding OU4, such as input on what the priority actions should be. An absurd twenty-year schedule for OU4 is specified, at which time the current EPA personnel will have moved on, and many of the locals who are vocal about the site may be deceased. There are some wonderful, caring citizens affected by this Superfund site. It looks like the only real actions they will see during their lifetimes are some of their neighbors moving away and their home towns disappearing. What a shame!

Earl Hatley
GRAND RIVERKEEPER
LEAD Agency, Inc.

When I took a look at the Tar Creek Superfund Site I knew this is going to be my last project. Here I am sixty, and they are predicting it will take over twenty years to complete it. I know it will be my last significant site.

It is the eighteenth Superfund site I have worked on, and this is the worst in terms of size and population of exposure. I have worked on some sites where the contaminants were more deadly—dioxin, hydrocarbons coming down in the air—with people getting cancers and kids dying.

I have been to some horrendous places, but this has the most environmental damage, it's the largest environmentally damaged area affecting the most people.

I've been an organizer for environmental issues for a very long time. Back in 1990, I was a regional organizer with the National Toxics Campaign for five states in the heartland region in the central US. One of the organizations I organized was the Oklahoma Toxics Campaign, and in 1993 I became the executive director. Oklahoma had eleven Superfund sites.

In 1994 Rebecca Jim called me and asked if my organization could sponsor her organization, the Cherokee Volunteer Society. This was not the typical grassroots group I was used to working with. These were high school kids, all of them. They were Rebecca's kids. Many were primarily affected by the site. These were the kids who were having trouble in school and who had low self-esteem as a result. While working with them, she established a Learn and Serve Project for Miami High School. They wanted to work on the Tar Creek site.

The Cherokee Volunteers organized the very first Tar Creek event that has become an institution—the Fish Tournament on Tar Creek and Toxic Tour. The tongue-in-cheek Earth Day event really wasn't a fish tournament, but the first few years we did have a fish fry.

The kids really wanted a fish tournament but that was not possible because of the pollution in Tar Creek. So the idea was that we were going to keep holding the fish tournaments until the day comes when we can actually get out there and have one. There have been thirteen fish tournaments so far.

In 1979 when the acid mine water surfaced and killed all the fish in Tar Creek all the way down to the Neosho River, the governor formed a task force. They did some studies, but no adults ever actually created a community group to deal with Tar Creek. This was very surprising. A whole decade went by, but there was still no community group at Tar Creek until those kids stepped up.

In 1997 I focused entirely on the Tar Creek site. The thing that stuck in my mind the most was that tribes were not involved, and there were eight tribes at that time immediately impacted by the site in Ottawa County. It was easy to see that the majority of the actual abandoned mines were in the jurisdiction of the Quapaw Tribe, yet at every EPA meeting I went to, I never saw a representative of the tribe.

One evening I was sitting next to the Quapaw tribal planner, John Gault. He had come to the meeting thinking that the tribe should be involved, although they were not at the time. Why not? Because they were never invited. He and I agreed that the Tar Creek site was never going to be cleaned up until the Quapaw Tribe and the other tribes were at the table making decisions with the EPA.

Gault applied for the general assistance program EPA was offering tribes to start environmental offices and also to make other grants available. I was hired to be the first environmental director for the Quapaw Tribe. This was in November 1997. I used all the techniques I had learned until that point to get the Quapaw Tribe to the table with the EPA. This was a really amazing project for me because of the government-to-government relationship tribes have with the EPA and with the federal government. Tribes have sovereignty, as dependent sovereign nations within the U.S.

In CERLCA, the Comprehensive Environmental Response Compensation and Liability Act, known as the Superfund

Act, there is a clause that makes tribes trustees over natural resources on tribal lands. That was really interesting to me because citizens groups were not trustees. Even though I had been immensely successful at getting citizens groups to the table to negotiate cleanup at other sites, I had to march, demonstrate and do media campaigns to make that happen.

Here I had the unique opportunity of organizing for a tribe, but it didn't mean it was an open road. Ultimately, the Quapaw Tribe got a water program, a Superfund program, an air quality program, and an emergency response program while I was working there—it took three years.

For the Tar Creek site, the tribes are important because they have jurisdiction within the abandoned mine area and also because the tribes downstream are affected. It is crucial that tribes got involved because of the power that they have with the EPA. It is a fact that the government-to-government relationship actually trumps the state's relationship. It really does.

Concerned citizens in other communities should know that the empowerment and the speed at which things get done are altogether different when tribes are involved. Any non-profit environmental group in any given state that can ally themselves with a tribe for the protection of the environment or to solve their issues should do that to the best of its ability. Develop an alliance and work together. Each has a unique path, and those paths are parallel and ultimately converge.

While the tribal environmental directors and tribal governments were getting their act together working to have a voice with EPA and the state, the other tribal efforts were the clanmothers and clanfathers. The grassroot groups were out there doing something about it. At the same time that yards were being cleaned up, the homes were being made safer because of the awareness efforts concerning how contaminated the dust was. The awareness was catching on.

The awareness created by the clanmothers and clanfathers was so effective that by the time the yard removal was done and the BLL's were retested and found to be not too far from the national average, no one knew what had had the biggest effect on lowering the blood leads, the awareness efforts or the yard removal. But in this case, the clanmothers and clanfathers and LEAD Agency really developed a personal relationship with the county health department people who got involved. You couldn't tell the difference. They were clanmothers and clanfathers too. It all worked out that way. I think that this was way cool.

Back in 1999 LEAD Agency was up and running, and we thought about having a conference to coincide with the Fish Tournament & Toxic Tour, like a 4-day event. We have had nine of those Tar Creek conferences. The whole thing was instigated by the Cherokee Volunteers, the kids at Miami High School.

Note: Waterkeeper Alliance is a grassroots advocacy organization founded in 1999. With 157 local programs that are dedicated to preserving and protecting rivers, lakes and other water bodies from polluters. Each Waterkeeper program is devoted to the preservation of specific watersheds. Robert F. Kennedy, Jr. serves as President of Waterkeeper Alliance.

Donna Gourd
Cherokee Nation
Learn & Serve Program

Back in December 2001 I was hired by the Cherokee Nation Education Department to "Learn and Serve." Little did I realize then how profoundly that phrase would come to influence my thinking and actions over the next five years.

The tribe had already been operating the Learn and Serve Program for seven years. Miami High School had, in fact, been one of the first schools to receive a sub-grant for service-learning from Cherokee Nation Learn and Serve in 1994. Rebecca Jim who, instinctively understood the power of student voice, had used the sub-grant to establish the Cherokee Volunteer Society, engaging students, community members and, eventually, Congressional leaders in the business of cleaning up Tar Creek.

Students learned science as they took water samples to measure the content of lead and other harmful elements left behind by mining decades earlier. They learned communication skills as they started examining and expressing their thoughts about the environmental impacts of industry. They learned to organize, plan and fulfill projects as they established the annual Tar Creek Conference in 1998. They learned about the functions of civics and government as they started attending city and tribal Council meetings and writing letters to elected leaders. They learned humanities as they expressed their feelings toward Ms. Jim, each other and the creek in photos, essays and poems published in the anthologies titled, *The Legacy,* and *Our Toxic Place.* They learned all of this as they served their school and community in any number of ways, from fund-raising to consciousness-raising, and they learned and served, as young people always do, because they revolved around a nucleus of kindness, concern, confidence and determination.

More than once over these past five-and-a-half years, as I have struggled to learn about federal program management—statistics and grant-writing, accounting and reporting, staff training and contract negotiation—I have been inspired by the friendship of Rebecca Jim and the example she and her students set. Although, at times, they were met with differences of opinion over what should be done, and on occasion they faced disappointment over what seemed like a lack of integrity, they persevered and stayed close to each other in spirit and in purpose.

Some of the students who were founding members of the Cherokee Volunteer Society have found relationships and careers out of their shared efforts. They have gone on to leave their own legacy around Tar Creek that, in so many ways, will outlive the poison and neglect. Rebecca tells me that, in the ten years since the Tar Creek Conference was established, the percentage of area children with high blood levels has been reduced from 42% to 4%. That's something! But it's not all.

In reclaiming the life of Tar Creek, as misshapen, discolored and toxic as it was, the Cherokee Volunteer Society succeeded in reminding us all that we are part of that life and it is a part of us. Our ancestors understood that every drop of blood running through the veins of every human being shares the same essence of creation, just as every drop of water in every stream on earth carries life-sustaining elements.

Since my first meeting with Rebecca Jim at Miami High School the year before she retired as counselor there, I have had the distinct privilege of working with many worthy school–community projects funded by the Cherokee Nation Learn and Serve Program. Certainly, the experience has taught me about the "business" of grant management. Far more deeply it has impressed me with the "art" of service-learning. The Tar Creek Project is a wonderful example of what can happen to individuals and groups who are able to move successfully through conflict or challenge because of heart-felt concern.

Through service we learn about ourselves and others. It is through service we learn about places and things. Through service we come to know our own place in our families, our communities and our world. Let us pray that the lessons of the Cherokee Volunteer Society and its relationship with Tar Creek will continue to influence the thoughts and actions of the people of Miami and the surrounding area.

Photo courtesy Cherokee Volunteer archives

Note: Service-learning is a method of teaching, learning and reflecting that combines academic classroom curriculum with meaningful service. The service meets authentic community needs. Service-learning combines experiential learning and community service opportunities.

Judith David
Language Arts Teacher
Miami High School
Learn and Serve Program

I saw young people blossom into maturity as they fought for a cause much bigger than themselves.

When I look back at my high school teaching career, I realize that working with Rebecca Jim and the Cherokee Volunteers was one of the most rewarding aspects of my teaching career.

I don't really know who said, "The pen is mightier than the sword," but it can be true. I just recently found out that the first *Tar Creek Anthology*, which I helped compile, set in motion a chain of events that resulted in the Tar Creek Task Force being formed. When my students, and students from other English classes, submitted their poems, essays, and research papers, no one dreamed that this little book would have such an effect.

Everyone who has ever been involved with the Tar Creek Project has added one little piece to the puzzle. We all knew that we were working on something good, something important. So many people worked on so many different aspects of the problem in so many different ways. All these years later, the children in the Tar Creek community have a chance of a better life than they might have had otherwise. I am so grateful that I had a chance to be a small part of it.

Mary Frayser
Cherokee Volunteer

**The Cherokee Volunteers started
an awareness effort and informed
thousands about what lead is
and why it was so dangerous.**

My role was to do whatever I could to help. I donated a tooth. I also have a piece of lead from my old driveway stuck in my hand forever where you can see it.

I think starting out with the students was important. The students then went home to their parents and friends, then the tribes got involved, then the whole community, just by showing that all of us had this one thing in common and that it affected each and every one of us. We showed that by combining all of these people we actually got something done.

If we hadn't come together for the cause, no one would have found out about the levels of lead and it would only continue to hurt and even kill our community.

Rebecca Jim started the Cherokee Volunteers who in turn followed her awesome lead to start awareness and help research. The elders started in the clanmothers and fathers organization and started donating for the cause. I think she should be recognized for all of her efforts. She definitely deserves to go down in history for it.

I hope to see that the blood lead levels reach zero in the future and that the homes and towns destroyed can be rebuilt on safe land. I remember when aunt Becky collected teeth to send to Harvard and people couldn't understand her wanting to do that and they weren't all very nice about all of her ideas and acted like it wasn't a very big deal. Even the principle made some comments that he later had to take back and I think he ended up apologizing for them as well.

Note: Mary Frayser was one of the original six Cherokee students at Miami High School to form the Cherokee Volunteer Society (CVS), a learn and serve organization sponsored by the Cherokee Nation.

**We inspire other communities
by showing when everyone comes
together, something can actually be
done to make your community
a better and safer place to live.**

Jessica Sage

Cherokee Volunteer

Pre-K Teacher
Picher Resident

Photo courtesy Jessica Sage

We told him they are basically just babies. They need a chance.

The thing that affected me most about being in the Cherokee Volunteer Society was when we actually went out in the communities, spreading the word and getting hands on, letting everyone know what was going on. That REALLY put everything into perspective for me.

If you talk about it but you never really do it, then it is never really real. I remember hanging the signs. That was my favorite part. We actually got to create those signs. We had drawings and we had a contest and we got to get those signs out in the public. It was something we had done; we took pride in it. We had an impact.

I still have pictures of the Tar Creek Fish Tournament and Toxic Tour. We had bands come and play, we brought a lot of people in that way, when you have something like that in the community. Having live bands interested others. We got publicity while they are spreading the word, and more bands wanted to get involved. It was so much fun. I still have my t-shirts. We tried to have fun and we had a little twist of irony in everything we did.

We used to go out to talk to schools. We got our pictures taken with the "Don't play on chat piles" signs in front of the post office, when we got permission from the Bureau of Indian Affairs to hang the signs on Indian-land since most of the chat piles were on Indian owned land. Honestly, I have seen the signs in some interesting places. I think people kept them as souvenirs.

We took pictures and the chat pile signs to schools and talked to them about how the water was contaminated and not to swim in it. I have pictures of when the *Washington*

Post came to interview us at the Little Angels Daycare. We had a large group of the four and five-year-olds, and the interviewer watched us as we talked to them. He asked why that was necessary. We told him, "they are basically just babies. They need a chance."

You cannot see the poisoning on the outside. Spreading the word wasn't necessarily a job, but in a way it was. It was something that needed to be done, and while I could do it, I wanted to do it.

I lived in Picher. We have just recently moved to Peoria, ahead of the buyout. We have not received our money yet, but we wanted to purchase the house and be ready for it, since you have only 30 days to close on a house once you get the notice to get out. So we went ahead and bought out. I think it has helped my mom a lot. Her health is getting better. Living in Picher was a lot of stress, and it is not a healthy climate; when the dust blows, it is dirty. You breathe in everything off the chat piles. One of the most amazing things that I have discovered after moving from Picher is just exactly how dusty it was inside the home.

You hear everyday on the news that people are afraid that they will be left behind and about the ones that don't want to move. If they only knew how badly it really affected their health, if the effects were more visible, then people would understand more.

It is amazing that I am not in high school anymore. I should still be going to school myself instead of getting kids ready for school. Now I think about that I am the one they are looking at and I'm scared half to death.

I did my student teaching at Wyandotte, and the school district decided to let me open the early childhood program. I put everything to use that I had learned at daycares and learning centers. I have a classroom and they allowed me to plan the space and the curriculum. It is amazing.

Lessons Learned....

I just recently joined the Peoria Volunteer Fire Department. A man really inspired me to join by saying, What if it was your family? What if it was someone you knew or what if it was you who could help them and save their life and make a difference? He said What would you do if you choose not to join and the fire is at your home and you needed us and there was no one here to come and save you? It made me think and realize that we can all make a difference, no matter how little or big, no matter how far away. If you could help someone, or save their lives, you would definitely make some sort of effort, especially if it involved someone that you cared about or knew.

To put Tar Creek in perspective, what if it was your family, what if it was someone you knew or your own friend?

Honestly, I have seen the signs in some interesting places. I think people kept them as souvenirs.

Deidra Bales, Carrie Montgomery and Jessica Sage stand with Bureau of Indian Affairs representative John Dalgarn the day they were given permission to post the warning signs on Indian trust land.

31

Chris Robinson
Cherokee Volunteer
Miami High School 1996 – 2000

I was somewhat of a misfit in high school and didn't fit in lots of places. Rebecca Jim came up to me one day and asked, "Why don't you get involved with the Cherokee Volunteer Society?" I checked it out and found the projects were pretty good, and I started to get interested. I was unaware at the time, but I was taking the first steps down a path that would have a profound influence, not only in my life but also in the lives of those around me. It ended up being one of the best things that ever happened to me.

I began to learn and understand what the issues were in the area. The biggest issue in the area was lead and zinc contamination from the mines. So I learned more about the mines and how the process worked with the water table, and the mines filling with water and lifting the contaminants out into our environment. So I joined Ms. Jim's grassroots movement, and I started getting involved with community education and raising the political awareness concerning this situation.

The things we did were so numerous that it is hard to know where to start. The number one thing we did that made an impact on our congressmen and in the education world was to hold the first Tar Creek Conference and get people to come speak and get experts to explain about the type of pollution in our area.

I remember one of Governor Keatings's Task Force meetings held on the stage at NEO College. I was debating one of the members. He and I were looking each other in the eye, getting into the situation, and him saying how things that hadn't happened were not the responsibility of the state and were not the responsibility of the mining companies that were associated with creating this pollution. He was head of the Oklahoma Department of Environmental Quality sitting there on the Governor's Task Force. We were debating head to head, and he was telling me I was wrong. Several other people, his compatriots, were standing up there saying that he was right. I recall being so frustrated when that debate was over that I had to take a few minutes to myself and step into another room.

I had serious levels of asthma from living in this area. It is very clear in my mind that the environment in Northeast Oklahoma had a direct impact on the way that I breathe. Occasionally, when exercising I would have asthma attacks. I would be sitting here when the winds were high, and the dust blowing around was kicked up into the air—that's what really got me. In other parts of the country, I have had hardly any issues whatsoever. I have lived in other places in Oklahoma like Stillwater, and I have lived in Colorado, where I was exposed to a different kind of environment. I even lived in New York City with its high level of pollution. I had not experienced asthma in any of those places.

My brother has a disorder called ADHD. The studies that have been done, especially with researchers from Harvard, show that heavy metal contamination has a direct correlation with both ADHD and asthma. He has felt alienated his entire life. He felt: "Something is wrong with me." My brother is one of the most generous, most intelligent person you will ever meet in your life. He has had to deal with ADHD all his life and has had very few people who understood his problem or were willing to talk about it. It caused him emotional and psychological stress that still affects him today, though not as drastically as when he was younger. He has matured and is happy and has learned to adapt to his condition, but it still affects his day-to-day life.

I'm truly thankful for the dedication of all the Cherokee Volunteers—the amount of effort put in by each student has been amazing—and for the opportunity to be a part of the cause. I treasure all the friendships I have made. Most of all, I will always remember Rebecca Jim, who is a truly inspirational and awe-inspiring person.

Note: Tar Creek runs through the length of the Robinson family land, stretching almost a mile in length. Chris's dad, Dr. Tom Robinson, received a Mike Synar Environmental Excellence Award posthumously for his vision of a clean Tar Creek and for allowing the first wetlands project to be initiated, as did George Mayer. That project is named for both men and has been designed by the Army Corps of Engineers.

It is very clear in my mind that the environment in Northeast Oklahoma had a direct impact on the way that I breathe.

Remembering....

The most memorable time for me was getting to meet the group who came from Harvard University. Dr. Howard Hu and his associates came down to speak to us. Here were professors all the way from Harvard—one of the best universities in the world—and they were coming to investigate our problem. Our problem was important to them, and they wanted to find out what was happening and how they could help. What could the possible solutions be? Who is affected by this?

Meeting Dr. Hu was really important to me. I had used some things he had written as evidence in one of my debate competitions when I was in high school. Here was someone I had been quoting for almost a year and using his knowledge in a competitive situation to my advantage, and to see the guy face to face was amazing.

Photo courtesy LEAD Agency, Inc. archives

Chris Robinson (center) with his brother and mother, after accepting the Mike Synar Award for his dad, Dr. Tom Robinson.

Cori Stotts Moore
Cherokee Volunteer
Parent

I remember when I first woke up to how dangerous this place might be. I was in seventh grade when my sister Lyndsi was diagnosed with leukemia. She got really, really sick. They ran tests on her and discovered that she had contracted giardia, which only comes through contaminated water. I was sitting in Mr. Kurtz's class, and I was just worried sick about her. That kind of blow to her immune system was a big thing at that time. It was dangerous and risky to her. I was having a hard time focusing, and he knew what the problem was. He told me, "You know who you need to talk to? Rebecca Jim." I had never met her before.

I went into Ms. Jim's office and she said, "We need to call and have the waters tested. It could be in the drinking fountains; it could be anywhere." Lyndsi is like the canary in the mine because her immune system is low; things that might not affect you and me could have a profound effect on her physically. She would get sick before anybody else. That was the first time I had ever been exposed to the fact that we had a problems in our environment. Until then it wasn't something that was talked about.

I read everything I could about leukemia. Lyndsi had acute lymphatic leukemia, and I always wondered about how where we lived contributed to her illness, even though they said that there were no environmental factors. Then I started putting together the pieces. I knew that the rate of that kind of cancer was 1 in 20,000; those were the odds. At the same time that Lyndsi was diagnosed, there had already been three others diagnosed with acute lymphatic leukemia in Miami, Oklahoma, not just Ottawa County. Plus there were numerous types of pediatric cancer in the area. I remember Lyndsi's doctor saying to me that he had wondered if it could be caused by environmental factors because there was an enormous rate of cancer in this little confined area. It was even more concentrated in the same neighborhood that we were in. At one point in time, another child diagnosed with acute leukemia lived in the same neighborhood as we did in the southeast portion of town. So it was scary. It was really scary. There are kids all over the country who have it, but nobody wanted to look at the fact that it occurred a lot here.

Lyndsi is in remission now, but she is still the canary in the mine. When we first moved here from Cushing, Oklahoma, my dad told us about the cool mountains of Picher that everyone talked about. Although my parents were really smart, responsible, and great parents, they took me to climb on these mountains of chat. Nobody knew about the dangers back then.

I met Ms. Jim before the Cherokee Volunteers were organized, but she was very aware of the problem even then. It seemed that no one else was paying attention. But Ms. Jim knew then that there was a problem. As I continued to investigate, I saw how many of the serious health problems in the area could be tied to the toxic environment. I talked to children whose moms and dads had worked in the mine. Many of the former miners were affected with black lung disease, as well as other related illnesses. Other than environmental factors, there is no explanation for an increased rate of many serious ailments, many of which have no known cure.

Later on, I became more and more involved in the Cherokee Volunteer Society. Chris Robinson and I went to Will Rogers Middle School and talked to every sixth grade science student. We talked all day long. That was a cool program. Those kids were really excited about what we told them about our environmental problems. They didn't know about it. They didn't have any idea. It was interesting to them. We were so motivated at that time and pumped, and they believed us.

Chris and I were a good team; we complimented each other really well. Each of us had a different aspect that we brought to it. He was more into the environmental part because he had Tar Creek running through his yard. So we had both the environment and health covered when we would go out. On top of that, we had fun.

I remember one particular Tar Creek Conference. Chris and I were getting more confident all the time. In the beginning we had people tell us that we wrong or try to convince us of something. But as we became more educated about the issues, the more we realized that some people were not being completely honest with us. At the conference, I remember somebody with a governmental environmental agency actually said that lead didn't blow. He was saying that lead didn't move in the air. I remember me and Chris itching in our seats, ready to pull him up out of the ground, waiting for this guy to get done talking. We thought to ourselves, "Are you kidding me?!" We could have gone through the ceiling because we were so mad. This guy talked like he was educated about it, and to anyone who had not been involved, he would have been really convincing. Most people probably did believe what he was saying. So it infuriated both of us. So we spoke up: "How do you find it in window sills? How does it get there? How can you say it doesn't blow when tornadoes move houses, and you say wind doesn't move lead? *ARE YOU SERIOUS*?"

He said, "No, it is too heavy for the wind to blow it." I remember we thought, You fool! Are you seriously going to try feed us that? We have gotten smarter. We have gotten better at this. Save it for somebody stupid. I remember Chris just continuing to say, "Answer my question!" We were coming into our own. Chris and I had figured things out and were more informed about the issues, and so it was harder for people to feed us baloney. I always wondered what that guy thought at that moment. He had to know he was lunch meat.

Chris and I had figured things out and were more informed about the issues, and so it was harder to feed us baloney.

Ryan Reeves
Cherokee Volunteer
LEAD Agency member
Parent

I didn't know much about what was happening with the environment until I got involved with the CVS. I really got started my sophomore year in high school, though I was interested in my freshman year. I attended the conferences. You should see my collection of name tags. I got interested because I like to help. We were promoting awareness through the media and testing.

We needed to make people aware, to get their attention, to write letters, make presentations, make posters and advertising, and go door to door. They didn't know what was going on. I wanted to be a part of that.

It gave me something to be involved with. It gave me something to look forward to. At the time, all I had was school. I wanted to do something to make my life more interesting as well as to help people. I wanted to help people, and I did.

Now that I'm out of school and working and am a single parent with a six-year-old, I always take off a week for the conference and don't get paid for it. Some people think I am crazy, but it is what I want to do.

Remembering....

As a kid I went to Nichols Elementary, and in first or second grade, I would go play in the chat every recess. I didn't know what it was. I just knew it made cool things. I had no idea that it was hurting me. You wouldn't think anything on the school grounds would hurt a child. That is why I really wanted to get involved, too. I wanted to wake up people and say, "This is here and shouldn't be."

I felt a great sense of gratification when the Nichols school playground was cleaned up. I see that we got something accomplished. I have gained a lot from all these experiences. I gained appreciation of the environment, that is for sure.

I wanted to do something to make my life more interesting, as well as to help people. I wanted to help people, and I did.

Photo courtesy LEAD Agency, Inc. archives

Shawn Williamson
Cherokee Volunteer

This was something I saw as a cause worth doing.

My sophomore year I got involved in the CVS. For the most part, I was never involved in anything throughout school. I was always a person off by myself, never the one to be around or do anything. I got tired of being so isolated. My friends asked me to go to a CVS meeting, and I kind of drifted in. The more I listened, the more I thought, this was something I see as a cause worth doing.

I helped Ryan with CVS cards and designs for badges. I helped with the brainstorming, the mental work, not the physical work. It was an ongoing process, and, on the way, you find something else that needs to be done. Pretty soon you have all these branches of projects going on at the same time.

We have so much work to do, we are never going to be done.

Photo courtesy LEAD Agency, Inc. archives

Samantha Proctor
Cherokee Volunteer
Ottawa County Deputy Court Clerk

I kind of grew up a little bit after finding out how dangerous it was.

My friend Jessica and I used to go and play on the chat piles and ride our four wheelers until we learned what the dangers were. I look back and say, "What was I thinking?" We drove our trucks on the chat piles and went at night with the dogs to let them chase raccoons. Jessica grew up there. That is just what they did. I didn't know any better.

I remember going down to Tar Creek and Picher. I had never really seen it before. I couldn't believe the brown water and the bridge that looked almost rotted. We went on the tour. We learned about the equipment below ground.

There was something else I had heard of but never seen—that yard at Commerce with the big sinkhole in it. I was just learning the whole story. I never knew what chat piles were when I was younger. I really didn't care until we started doing all the research and looking into it. Then it really opened my eyes and helped me see the problem. We figured it out. Mr. Bradley, the high school science teacher was doing wetlands research and learning about phytoremediation.

We were so fortunate to have the opportunities and experiences. I wish people would take the time to learn about Tar Creek. I was stupid to it. I had no idea. Once we started learning, my eyes were opened. Because of the Cherokee Volunteer Society, a lot more people know about Tar Creek now. That is a payoff.

Photo courtesy Jessica Sage

Jessica Sage and Samantha Proctor

I remember going down and looking at that bridge and at that water. I couldn't believe it.

39

Georgeann Roye

Miami High School Graduate
Harvard Graduate
Miami High School Teacher

I grew up looking at red water.

I grew up in a house probably 150 yards from Tar Creek. Tar Creek overtook the house with about four feet of water. FEMA says the house will be condemned. So in addition to Tar Creek polluting itself with lead and heavy metals, there are the compound issues of the dam and the lake and the backup of the excess water. As we know in Miami, floods rarely happen because of water rushing through; they almost always happen because of water backing up from the Neosho River.

On my last working day at Miami High School, introducing the instructor of my last science class at Harvard made it a full-circle day. My next step is law school.

Dr. Joseph Brain taught Human Organism at Harvard, a basic science class for non-majors. I waited to take it in my senior year. We focused on the nervous system, the reproductive system and other major systems of the body. It was a fascinating class. I am not a science person, but I was totally drawn in. I could tell my students, once I became a teacher, about the times I got to handle human hearts of people who had donated their organs. In one lab we got to handle hearts from a healthy person, an obese person and a smoker. That made it very hands-on.

Now, as an English instructor at my own high school, the school that propelled me on to a successful experience at Harvard, I have been taking part in the Tar Creek Project as an instructor, no longer the student. Dr. Brain is now doing research here at Tar Creek on the effects of multiple metals exposures. He came to my school library to talk about his local research conducted in the Children's Center project.

In my first year of traditional classroom teaching, I was in a state of emergency and taking what was at hand, and what was at hand in my classroom was that set of Barbara Kingsolver books, *Pigs in Heaven* and *The Bean Trees*. My little freshmen had never attempted that kind of novel, 300-plus pages but easy prose. Both books start and end here in Oklahoma, and in conjunction with the stories, which involve the Cherokee Tribe, we extrapolated that this was a way of telling the Cherokee story. And that raised the question of how we could also learn something about the other nine tribes that were relocated to Ottawa County. So their task was to research in pairs, choose one of the nine tribes and either write about an environmental issue or a historical issue. They had to tie it to or draw a parallel to the story told in the Barbara Kingsolver books, specifically in *Pigs in Heaven*. One of the characters is Anawake, an attorney, and at some point she tells the history of the Cherokee people. My students had to find out how the tribe they chose got here, how the Modocs got here, how the Shawnees got here, and it had to show up in their papers.

The students wrote their first research papers, and then had

the opportunity to take part in the Toxic Tour bike ride that originated at the Miners Reunion Park in Picher. Over fifty riders took part, many my students and their parents. Each wrote a reflection paper about that experience, each touched by what they learned. That park is now fenced off to the public due to the risk of cave-ins.

Note: When Georgeann was a student at Miami High School, her poem, *Fish Kisses*, was published in the *Tar Creek Anthology: The Legacy*. The poem recalls a day at Lost Creek and may have helped spur the efforts to reclaim the creek, as recounted by Glenna Wallace.

Tom Lindley
The Oklahoman
Journalist

I'm not sure how or why the copy of the *Tar Creek Anthology* wound up on my desk not long after I started work at *The Oklahoman*. Maybe it was part of the initiation ceremony—"Let's see if the new guy will fall on his face trying to find a new way to write about the futile attempts to clean up the Tar Creek Superfund Site."

All I know is that once I started reading the poems and essays written by Miami High School students who were members of the Cherokee Volunteers Society, I couldn't stop. They spoke of a river without fish, of an endangered culture, of environmental injustice, of a land that seemed as far away as the moon. I wondered, "Was it the innocence of youth speaking or did their haunting words hold real significance?" By the time I stopped reading, I knew I had to find out for myself.

And so began my journey to shed new light on Tar Creek. I started out in the fall of 1999 to learn more about a river that had turned orange with toxic minerals but ended up fascinated about the fate of those along its banks, all the way to Grand Lake, the imperial body of water in Oklahoma, and the proud miners who came before.

A symbol of the turbulence that marked the twentieth century—from the decade of discovery in the early 1900s to a generation of neglect at the end—the hideous water of Tar Creek was impossible to ignore. But it was the beautiful faces of the innocent, young children of Picher and Cardin, who were being exposed to lead in the air and on the ground, that made the story real.

The Oklahoman told the story in a bold three-part newspaper series, splashed across the front page and accented by powerful pictures by photographer Steve Sisney. That was the easy part. As for the hard work, well, credit for that has to go to two groups: the students of Miami High and their counselor, Rebecca Jim, and others in the community who refused to accept their fate. The other heavy lifting came from an unlikely source, Governor Frank Keating, who waded in where few politicians would dare tread, given that there was far greater political risk than there was reward for coming to the rescue of a largely poor, neglected community.

Governor Keating's Tar Creek Task Force helped switch the focus from the inadequate remediation of yards to the real health needs of the children and the risks to the community at large. His successor, Governor Brad Henry, with the assistance of Secretary of Environment Miles Tolbert and J. D. Strong, continued to coordinate efforts to reach a consensus between the bureaucrats and a skeptical public.

That is not to say that the scars on the land have completely healed, revealing the beauty of the prairie as it once appeared and making the people who were ground up in the name of progress whole again.

But the people did speak out against a river that ran orange, and those in power did pay attention. That's a powerful story.

Photo by Vaughn Wascovich

This photograph caught the attention of the *Time* Magazine journalist who increased national attention to Tar Creek.

J. D. Strong
Chief of Staff
Office of the Secretary of the Environment

Words cannot describe this place.

It is an oft-used phrase, but never more fitting than when used to describe Tar Creek. Our environmental agency personnel often tried to describe the calamity, but never in a way that screamed for attention beyond what other Superfund sites in Oklahoma were getting. Countless residents of Tar Creek tried to communicate their horror, as did many great journalists, but to no avail. Put simply, "Words cannot describe this place!"

Then along came a picture. I distinctly remember the picture on the front page of *The Oklahoman* of four-year-old Ashley and two-year-old Chad sitting in the front yard of their home in Picher, both suffering neurological damage from elevated blood lead levels. It was that picture that turned the tide for Tar Creek, along with a related series of front-page articles, all of which collectively painted a vivid picture in our minds that something was awry in the far northeastern corner of Oklahoma. Something more than the normal, perfunctory Superfund Program course of action had to be done.

Secretary of the Environment Brian Griffin and I were summoned by Governor Frank Keating in December 1999, only days after the picture and series ran. Governor Keating gripped the picture in his hands and asked us how something like this could happen in Oklahoma. It was clear that he would not sit idly by and watch future generations of Oklahomans be poisoned and permanently impaired by the legacy of lead and zinc mining that led to the nation's highest ranking Superfund site being assigned to Tar Creek. We were to get to work on bringing all of the state's resources to bear on this issue, starting with the creation of a task force to study the lingering concerns at Tar Creek and propose holistic solutions.

Less than a month later, in January 2000, Governor Keating's Tar Creek Superfund Task Force was formed by Executive Order 00-02, and the ten-member panel was given an ambitious ten month deadline to accomplish its mission. Without question, Governor Keating expected prompt and thorough attention to this urgent matter. Ten-months and many arduous hours of research and deliberation later, the Task Force and its eight subcommittees had compiled the most comprehensive catalog of the myriad health, safety, and environmental problems persisting at Tar Creek, as well as proposed solutions for addressing them.

The final report included a novel, albeit controversial, concept for solving the majority of the most imminent risks at Tar Creek in one fell swoop. The Task Force's overarching vision was to relocate the residents of the most heavily impacted areas in and around Picher and Cardin, then reclaim the site as a "world-class wetlands area and wildlife refuge" centered on the most promising remediation technology proffered by experts for this mega-site—engineered wetlands to treat contaminated mine discharges and other contaminated runoff. While the Task Force's vision for a world-class wetlands area and wildlife refuge was never completely embraced by the federal government or congress, which ultimately would have to devote the resources necessary to solve Tar Creek's problems, the Task Force's work was nevertheless invaluable in setting a number of things in motion. First and foremost, the nation's highest ranking Superfund site finally received the national attention that it deserved. Prominent stories ran in the *New York Times* and *Washington Post*, and Tar Creek's obstinate health and environmental problems were even featured on ABC's *Nightline*. In less than one year, Tar Creek grew from a little nuisance in the far northeastern corner of Oklahoma to the country's worst environmental disaster, where over a hundred million dollars in Superfund monies had been spent with nary a dent made in the work left to do.

Second, the Task Force's final report marked the first time that the State of Oklahoma embraced the idea that relocation of residents from the most ravaged areas was the only way to guarantee their protection from the perils of Tar Creek. There was recognition that decades would be needed to implement any ultimate solution, which meant that those at greatest risk must be afforded a way out now. Just as important was the acknowledgment that there must be final resolution. The vision of restoring the area to a wetlands and wildlife area showed strong support from the highest levels of state government that Oklahomans would not settle for anything less than a complete healing of this ravaged landscape.

Momentum and national attention on Tar Creek continued to build in the wake of the Governor's Task Force. Within a few years, Oklahoma elected a new Governor, Brad Henry,
who was convinced by his newly appointed Secretary of the Environment, Miles Tolbert, that interest in Tar Creek should never wane. In fact, Governor Henry determined to make resolution of Tar Creek one of his top priorities, a topic that he raised in each of his first several "State of the State" addresses. At roughly this same time, Oklahoma's most senior United States Senator, Jim Inhofe, had ascended to Chairman of the Environment and Public Works Committee, a position that gave him great power over the Federal agencies and appropriations necessary to properly address Tar Creek.

In his first major action concerning Tar Creek, Governor Henry let his sympathy for the young children suffering permanent neurological damage by living in Tar Creek's lead-infested environment get the best of him. Increasingly weary of the Federal government's apathy toward relocating residents from Tar Creek, Governor Henry resolved to secure state funds and resources to get them out of harm's way himself. He would wait no longer for the federal government to solve our problems.

On May 26, 2004, Governor Henry signed the Lead-Impacted Communities Relocation Assistance Act, which authorized the buy-out of families with children under the age of seven living within the most impacted area of Tar Creek. He secured $3 million from the Oklahoma legislature to accomplish this task and vowed to hold the federal government accountable for finishing the job that he was starting. Before the end of 2005, fifty-one families with young children had for the future well-being of their young children. a new lease on life, with no more fear. During this same time period Senator Inhofe recognized that it was

Oklahoma Governor Brad Henry signs the relocation bill.

going to take more than a bully pulpit to secure the tens of millions of dollars necessary to complete a buy-out of all residents in the epicenter of the Tar Creek site. Therefore, he secured funding for the Corps of Engineers to coordinate with others in the scientific community to study the abandoned mines, as well as those that had already collapsed, to determine the probability of future collapses at the site—a risk that heretofore had only been presumed.

January 31, 2006, became another defining day in the long Tar Creek saga as the subsidence study was released, which showed many areas in and around Picher and Cardin that had greater than 50% probability of collapse, some at depths greater than fifty feet. While everyone knew the governor's position on relocation as the most expedient relief measure, the public release of the report was coupled with an announcement that Senator Inhofe also would consider relocation in light of the dire safety risks presented in the report. Now joining forces, Senator Inhofe, Governor Henry, and

Congressman Boren announced plans to redirect all available Tar Creek remediation funds for a complete buy-out of the towns of Picher and Cardin, following the model employed by the state in 2004-2005. At last, the most heavily impacted people living within the Tar Creek Superfund Site would get the relief they so sorely deserved. While this more comprehensive buy-out is still in its early stages as this book is written, and all of the funding has yet to be secured to complete the job, the long-suffering people of Tar Creek finally have a glimmer of hope that they will be neglected no longer.

Coupled with this buy-out effort is a steady resolve on the part of Oklahoma's highest officials, as well as officials from the affected tribes, to ensure that the vision for a fully restored ecosystem comes to fruition. All levels of government, as well as all participating stakeholders, fully realize that the spotlight shines brightly on Tar Creek. Therefore, no one can walk away in the dark of night and leave this site to fester for decades. Never again!

So that is how it all started, with a picture—a picture that got the attention of the governor, who in turn got the attention of America. Now we are starting to see some real progress at the nation's highest-ranking Superfund site.

And God willing, it will soon end with a picture. Someday soon, I hope all we have left of the infamous Tar Creek Superfund Site is pictures of what it once was. By then, people from all over the region will be flocking to bask in its unprecedented tall grass meadows, with its prairie potholes, paw-paws, and waterfowl. Oh, and let's not forget about the superior fishing in pristine Tar Creek.   That is MY picture.

Photo by Earl Dotter

49

Photo courtesy TEAL archives

When we started working here in the 1990s, there weren't many other players at all. People hadn't heard of the lead contamination at Tar Creek, despite its shocking devastation. When you see it, you can't believe the entire country, as well as the entire world, doesn't know about it.

Michelle Kegler

TEAL Principal Investigator

Associate Professor
Department of Behavioral Science Health Education
Rollins School of Public Health. Emory University

I first became involved with efforts in the Tar Creek area in early 1996 in my first year as an assistant professor in the Department of Health Promotion Sciences at Oklahoma University Health Sciences Center. With colleague Bob Lynch, I became part of developing a grant proposal for an educational video on Tar Creek and lead exposure through the federal department of Occupational and Environmental Health (OEH). I wanted to include a lay advisor intervention component. That seed grew into TEAL and its clanmothers and clanfathers. I was asked to be the principal investigator on the project since it would have a strong community engagement/health education component.

One of the first steps was to visit Ottawa County and the tribes to see if they would like to work with us on this proposal. Three of us went to visit the chiefs and chairmen of the eight tribes. Tim Tall Chief, a member of my department, went with us to help bridge any cultural differences and to advise us on interacting with the chiefs. I remember him telling us to be very deferential and respectful because it was parallel to meeting with the President of the United States. All those we met with supported the project.

During this trip, I saw chat piles for the first time and was absolutely amazed. It looked like a moonscape and seemed almost impossible that it was created by man. Lorraine Malcoe, a social epidemiologist and another assistant professor at the College, also became interested in working on the project. She was a great asset because she wrote the whole blood lead screening part of the proposal.

In the spring of 1996, the Oklahoma State Department of Health learned that we were interested in working in Tar Creek. They had been approached by several mining companies to conduct the Community Health Action Monitoring Program (CHAMP), but they couldn't easily contract with mining companies. Ken Caderet of OSDH, the Oklahoma State Department of Health, called me, and I referred him to Lorraine. Since much of CHAMP's emphasis was on blood lead screening, we thought it looked like a good project since it involved a population-based blood lead screening phase and follow-up education for families who had children with elevated blood lead levels in Picher, Cardin and Quapaw.

A major event I recall about CHAMP was a community meeting in the Picher gym where Lorraine presented blood lead results. I did the door prizes, which was fun. Nancy Niehaus, a local employed with the project, designed our first calendar, which later became kind of an annual TEAL tradition. Susan Waldron and I developed the family education component. Susan did three follow-up visits with all the families in Picher and Cardin who had children with elevated blood lead levels. Susan organized a poster contest and the winning designs were put on t-shirts. I still wear mine.

Over time, our relationship with the mining companies soured. They wanted us to ask the EPA to halt the cleanup where we were doing CHAMP to see if education alone would make cleanup unnecessary. We refused. Then in August of that year, the grant we had applied for was funded through National Institutes of Environmental Health Sciences (NIEHS). We were so excited! And the work began. We hired Sally Whitecrow-Ollis. She was connected to the local Native American community plus had experience doing programs with tribal government.

One of the early activities was to establish a Community Advisory Board (CAB). Early on they picked the name for the project: TEAL—Tribal Efforts Against Lead. They advised us on the progress of the blood lead screening. Calling the lay health advisors clanmothers was Sally's idea. She seemed like an ideal clanmother. We ran it by the CAB members to make sure that using the idea in this way was okay with them. The first blood lead level screening was conducted in the summer and fall of 1997. The data was quickly analyzed and presented at a community meeting in Picher.

The CAB members were highly involved in training the clanmothers. They wrote major sections of the training manual and led major portions of the two-day training held in March of 1998. The clanmothers met monthly over the course of the two-year intervention. We had potlucks at various tribal buildings, which we rotated among tribes. At these meetings we planned our group activities. I was very grateful to Rebecca Jim and Earl Hatley at these meetings because they were always up to date on the policy and agency actions affecting Tar Creek and were our main sources of ideas for what we could do collectively. Susan Waldron was also good at generating ideas for us.

The clanmothers did all kinds of great things: TEAL coloring books, calendars with lead messages and tribal languages, educational booths at powwows and community events, letter-writing campaigns to support chat regulations and state support for Superfund cleanup, attendance at city council and county commissioners meetings to support regu-

lation of chat, letters to the editor, and so on.

We were active both in one-on-one education of the public and in educating decision makers.

In late 1999, it was time to write another grant to continue TEAL. Our project officer said we couldn't do the exact same thing. He said that we had to have a new idea. So we planned to expand to study the effect that heavy metals have on the environment. If Oklahoma University found significant levels of arsenic, mercury and zinc, we considered the possibility of adding a youth component. The idea was that the clanmothers would collaborate with Native American youth groups to do community education. Our proposal was successful, and we received an additional five years of funding. Since I had by then moved to Atlanta and taken a position at Emory University, I planned to step back a bit and have local staff run the project. I hired Kristin Thomas to serve as project director for this phase. She was instrumental in getting the youth component of the project off the ground.

Another blood lead level screening was undertaken in 2000. By this time, Lorraine Malcoe, epidemiologist with CHAMP and TEAL, had also relocated. Although Lorraine directed the screening, Mary Happy was hired to manage the screening locally. It seemed to go pretty smoothly, given how difficult and complicated these screenings were. We presented the results at a community meeting in March 2001. This time around there were twenty-four Native American lay health advisors who were recruited as clanmothers and clanfathers. They were all trained in lead poisoning awareness in September 2001.

Twenty remained active through the end of the intervention period, which was September 2003. Over the next two years, they educated their family and friends about lead poisoning and met monthly to plan education strategies. They reached over 12,500 people and spent over 3,500 hours on the project. The highlight for me was when they asked a county commissioner to stop spreading chat on rural roads, and he agreed to stop.

The clanmothers and clanfathers participated in many community events and also sponsored the cultural night at the National Tar Creek Conference in 2002, as well as the conference's Toxic Tour bicycle event in 2003.

In addition, TEAL and the clanmothers sponsored or assisted with several summer camps for children, including the Eastern Shawnee camp, Wyandotte Bearskin camp and the Picher Camp. At each of the camps, four or five clanmothers and clanfathers volunteered and assisted with the kids. Every activity was connected to something related to protecting youth from lead poisoning.

The Picher-Cardin students called their group Student Efforts Against Lead (SEAL), and the Quapaw students named their group Quapaw Unites Against Pollution and Waste (QUAPAW).

Youth projects included holding a poster/billboard contest, placing hand-washing stickers in public restrooms, writing letters to government leaders, hosting two nineteen-mile interactive toxic bicycle tours, preparing a nutritious foods cookbook with lead poisoning prevention messages, and putting on a community health fair. In 2003-2004, sixty-nine Quapaw students continued their work with the TEAL project. Their efforts focused on developing a housecleaning video and sponsoring the annual Toxic Tour.

I want to say again that there were a couple of people who made a huge difference over time—Rebecca Jim and Earl Hatley. We were dependent on and grateful to them. They knew the players, knew what needed to be done and what could be done. They knew what it took to create change. They were very effective in being resource people throughout because they were able to keep tabs on everybody and knew what needed to happen. They were absolutely critical to any success that happened here.

Note: Dr. Kegler and her colleagues have written a number of articles based on experiences and results from the involvement with Tar Creek. They are listed in the bibliography.

I think the lesson for other community activists who feel overwhelmed by environmental issues is to keep going and keep making connections.

Robert A. Lynch
TEAL Co-Investigator
Associate Professor
Occupational and Environmental Health
University of Oklahoma Health Sciences Center

At the beginning of my involvement, I was just starting my career as a college professor and now I find myself somewhere in the middle of my career, still dealing with the ramifications of what we found and accomplished and contemplating where to go next.

Before Tar Creek, I had worked on a number of projects across Oklahoma funded by state and federal programs, and they always required an element of local involvement, which was small or completely lacking in many cases. So this was the attitude with which I approached the first Tar Creek project, and my feelings about the level of public participation we might enjoy were pessimistic. My biggest reward in all of this was that I was wrong—way wrong.

My job at Tar Creek has been in taking environmental samples and trying to interpret what they tell us about exposures to lead from air, water, soil, dust, and paint. We all knew fairly early on that the situation was a mess from the standpoint that most people were exposed to lead from many sources. Even so, it was clear to all (or almost all) that those mammoth piles of mine wastes were the ultimate cause of the problem. The wastes were and are everywhere and the laboratory analysis of our samples showed them to contain very high levels of lead. Lead was in the yards and, more important, in the dust inside the homes where exposure to young children was and is a certainty.

The biggest human exposure problem at the Tar Creek Superfund site is lead contaminated soil and dusts. There can be no doubt that most of this came from the tens of millions of cubic yards of mine wastes.

Our leaders have commendably found a way to get children out of the area, and that should be heralded as a wonderful and long overdue victory. I can only hope that this effort has generated some momentum that will keep us going until we address the cleanup side of the problem. I know that I am not the first, but at least I want to be recorded as another person who recognized the long-term problem that this site poses for other areas, specifically downstream locations like

Grand Lake, and stress the need to fix this problem.

I am not a hydrologist but have enough common sense to know that the bulk of the mine wastes (minus that tiny fraction that blows into Kansas and out of the watershed) will all end up in Grand Lake.

Over the years, things have gotten better, primarily as measured by the ever-decreasing number of children with elevated blood lead levels. There have been many activities and many parties that have contributed to the improvement.

I will focus on what I know best, which is the environmental side of things. Cleanup of yards, roads, and common areas, and those who have worked for funds to accomplish this, should be given their fair recognition, as there can be no doubt that they are in part responsible for the improvement.

So let me be clear on this: The EPA efforts to remove contaminated materials from the Tar Creek Superfund site decreased the levels of exposure of children to lead.

We know about some of the problems this has caused, but it should still be judged as a good idea overall. It should also be noted that EPA took decisive action early, way before the state was able or willing to. They showed considerable leadership in this regard and did what they thought would make things better (and they were right). Of course, it would have been better and more cost-effective to have just moved

people out earlier, but this effort didn't begin until ten years after EPA started their cleanup work. How many more children would have been exposed without their efforts?

I would like to be able to attribute the success to some quantifiable attribute (a fault of most academicians), and I would be willing to bet that there is some measure that can be used—maybe something like an "Index of Community Spirit" on a scale of 1 to 10, with 10 being *very spirited* and 1 being *completely apathetic*.

I am not even sure where the boundaries of this community are—there probably isn't a physical or psychological boundary. With this in mind, I would give the Tar Creek community a very high Community Spirit score.

So my final point is, the main reason why things have gotten better at the Tar Creek Superfund Site is the spirit of the community and the diligent involvement that this has generated.

For my part, I have viewed myself as a provider of information for the community, and others outside the community, to put to good use, and I hope that I have contributed in a positive way. My involvement has been very rewarding both professionally and personally. I suspect (and hope) that it will continue. I hope that my words add one more piece to the mosaic of what has transpired.

Lorraine Halinka Malcoe

TEAL Co-Investigator

Associate Professor
Health Sciences
Simon Fraser University

What especially piqued my interest was the Indian Health Service data that suggested that Native American children might have a much worse problem. That was particularly concerning to me. That was part of my reason to get involved.

Michelle Kegler and Bob Lynch had been working together before I got involved. I went to lunch with Michelle, and after talking to her about Tar Creek, I was interested. She was going to resubmit a grant request to EPA and then to the National Institute of Health Sciences, NIHS. After looking it over, I thought there were some aspects I could strengthen as an epidemiologist.

The mining companies went to the county health department and wanted to give them the money for the community health monitoring program and education, but the county was under a hiring freeze and couldn't hire any one to do the work. So they approached Michelle and Bob, who had worked with the Quapaws, and asked if they would do it.

CHAMP was very important work. But the mining companies took some harmful actions. They wanted Susan Waldron, the health educator, to have the families ask EPA to delay the cleanup of the yards. When I told them that that was totally unethical, they threatened to pull the money.

The mining companies were actively trying to delay cleanup. It was outrageous. We couldn't believe it. They delayed the release of our information. We were finally able to have a big community meeting. I wrote the draft of the report, and they wanted to change a number of things that I would not change. I was tired of fighting with them. There was a draft report, and people got that. As far as I am concerned, the draft *is* the final report.

The whole team went on to TEAL. Michelle was the principal investigator. We worked really well together, and it didn't take much to keep us together. There was no competition among us. Bob's specialty was the environmental aspect and all the environmental data. I brought more epidemiological study design, and Michelle was the intervention and health promotion expert. We each had a role, and it worked perfectly for the project.

Our response rate in 1997 was a little over 50%—we wanted a much higher response rate. We did things differently for the data collection in 2000. We put more articles in the newspaper. Our response rate did go way up. But I think the biggest reason that it went up was that TEAL had a very big presence in the community. People recognized it and people trusted us. It is really important to be integrated into the community. If you are going into a community new or into a rural community, it is particularly important.

In the mining communities, we had close to the same rate of participation both years. It is very hard to get people to understand that the lead problem is not just in the mining area. It is a problem everywhere the chat has gone. In 1997 a lot of people in Miami felt like the problem was only in the mining area. Finding the problem in the air ducts in Miami awakened a lot of people. We had more people participating in Miami in 2000. That was the reason the response rate was higher, over 81.6%.

The three of us had fun working and traveling together. We collaborated on all the projects and had developed a camaraderie. It was fun to keep seeing the people we had developed relationships with.

Lessons Learned....

We were busy with all of our other work and traveling, but to me, this was one of the most meaningful research projects I have participated in. I felt like I had actually made a difference. I learned a lot from doing it. I learned how to ask research questions that had importance in policy relevance at a local community level. I wasn't taught how to ask those kinds of research questions at school.

Photo courtesy TEAL archives

Children six years old and under had their blood lead levels measured.

When you build relationships, you don't only do it for the community, you do it because it matters to you as well.

57

Children at daycares in Ottawa County received kits to encourage hand washing.

Susan Waldron
Ottawa County Health Department

"Nothing's been done here. All this money has been spent and nothing's been done." They're wrong.

We had so many different grants, so many different people, so many pieces, so many different organizations, and so many different projects going on at the same time, with so many people dedicated to their piece of the project. All of a sudden we had a pie, and we didn't even realize it.

As a public health educator in Miami, OK, I am currently in charge of the lead poisoning prevention program in Ottawa County, a program to teach children and adults about the dangers of lead poisoning.

I moved to Ottawa County in 1996 because my in-laws lived in the area. My husband and I both came up here without jobs. We had young children. I picked up the newspaper and found the University of Oklahoma was looking for a research assistant for a project because of lead poisoning in the area. And I said, "I can be a research assistant."

I knew nothing about lead poisoning or why they would be looking for it in the area. So I looked into everything I could find out about it. Did I know that it could be a problem here when I moved to this area? No, my in laws were from the southern part of Ottawa County. Could you see the chat piles from there? No. Did I know they were there when I moved here? No. Did I learn a lot about it by moving to the area? Not necessarily from just moving here. But working with

that research project opened up a whole new horizon, a whole new education for me. Did I want to tell everyone I met? Yes. There was a potential for harm to their children and themselves. I wanted to let them know about it.

Here's how it is about lead. First of all, lead is a neurotoxin. That means it is toxic to our neurological systems. It is most dangerous to children aged six and under, because is that is when our neurological systems are still developing. We looked at the CDC's guidelines—the magic number was 10 micrograms per deciliter (μg/dL) of lead in the blood or under is considered safe. Anything below ten was seen as within normal range. Anything above was too high, an action or alert level.

Don Ackerman was an environmental specialist at the Indian Health Center in 1994. His findings from the records showed that well over 30% of the children were high. Concerned, he sent letters alerting the EPA and the state health department and ATSDR, the Agency for Toxic Substances and Disease Registry, to look into this. The state health department sent out some nurses and they tested one hundred children. They found the same percentage of kids had elevated blood lead levels (BLL's).

Then the mining companies got involved. They said, "No, wait a minute; it could be lead-based paint. That is a big thing." That is true. All across the country, lead-based paint is an issue. There are lawsuits about the poisoning of children and adults by lead-based paint in homes. We do have these issues. So the mining companies wanted to look at all the sources of lead that might be available. They funded a project with the University of Oklahoma in 1996 called the

CHAMP Project: the Community Health Action Monitoring Program, and I became the research assistant.

The program was a comprehensive door-to-door project in the mining communities of Picher, Cardin, Quapaw, Commerce and North Miami. Going door to door, we'd ask people, "If you have children under six, would you let us draw their blood? Would you let us come in your home and do some dust sampling, soil sampling, water sampling, paint sampling? Would you let us do some education and tell you all the sources of lead poisoning that might be in your home?" It lasted for an entire year. And 43% of those kids had a ten or above. That was an alarm, a shout: *LISTEN, PEOPLE IN THESE COMMUNITIES!*

When the EPA Record of Decision (ROD) came out in 1997, yard cleanups started because the soil in yards around homes were found to have high levels of lead. This action was not caused by the CHAMP project results. It was already ongoing.

Also in 1997 the National Institute of Environmental Health Sciences funded TEAL. All of these things happening at the same time started increasing awareness. The BLL's started coming down almost immediately; I see this in retrospect. Hindsight is 20/20.

When we thought about how to increase awareness, we felt like we needed some help. We needed the children to recognize a mascot, but we didn't have any idea on how to come up with a mascot. In doing the lead testing, we would say to the kids, "It will be really quick, just a stick on your finger and it will hurt just for a second and it will be over." One

little girl said – like a bee? I said yes, just like a little bee. We were laughing that we should make the mascot a bee. We had a little boy who drew us a bee. His name was Dustin. He said, "Here's a bee for you. We could name him Lead-Free the Bee."

"Lead Free the Bee, lead free is the way to be"—that became our motto. We took a puppet theatre to the daycares and head starts with this little bee puppet. It went over phenomenally. The kids just went wild. We had bee flowers and my husband's aunt made us bee aprons and bee antennae. My husband shook his head over all this, but I told him, "I am having the time of my life."

The children came up and wanted to hug the bee and hold him. They would stand in line to get their finger stuck to hug him. It was the greatest thing ever. Kids asked how long until they could get it stuck again! Phenomenal. It helped so much. We went from being able to do 300-400 finger sticks a year to over a 1000.

I did a puppet show at one of the Tar Creek Conferences, and we had made up a little song about Lead Free, the Bee. I think I was filling in for someone else who didn't come, so I willingly sang this song. I don't sing. I want you to know this. There I was with the antennae on and the puppet on my hand and the Governor of Oklahoma walked in. I was singing the Lead Free song. So I have done things no one should be caught doing—but all for the cause of awareness, for Lead Free, the Bee.

We also had the mobile unit from the hospital and parked it at the WAL-MART parking lot and other public places.

That helped us to do screenings outside the health department.

EPA funded us though ATSDR for awareness education and blood lead screening to continue while they did yard cleanup. They have extended this funding on a yearly basis, until this day. This has been an awesome gift from the EPA.

Hand washing has been and is still one of the most powerful messages we teach kids. Even though I know in many places in the United States they say that can't possibly be the most important message you tell people, but it is. Hand to mouth is the way kids get lead into their bodies. That is why kids around the age of two and under are the most susceptible to lead poisoning. They put everything into their mouths. We teach kids at a very early age the benefits of hand washing.

We did a sweep of all the elementary schools. We did hand-washing clinics and made up hand-washing buckets for all those kids. There was a little towel with "Lead Free" on it, their own little soaps, and even a little nailbrush. So we went out and taught each one of them to wash their hands and the importance of washing. There was a little strap on the bucket, so they would all have their own buckets to hang in their bathrooms and so they could sing the little song, the ABC's. You would not believe how many parents called to say, "My child has to have a place for the bucket and everything has to be in there, perfect."

People say here all the time, "Nothing's been done here. All this money has been spent and nothing's been done." They're wrong. Some great things have been done here. The percentage of children with elevated blood lead levels has gone from 43% to less than 4% in less than a ten-year period. That just doesn't happen anywhere. The awareness has gone from, "I've lived here all my life, there isn't anything wrong with me" to, "We all need to do something about this."

It didn't just happen. Look at the people who all worked together, the synergy. What's happened here hasn't happened other places because every other place has a time line... a time restraint. You cannot put time restraints on synergy. You have to give credit to everyone: to the next door neighbors, to the lay health advisors, to EPA, to ATSDR, to LEAD Agency, and the list goes on and on because everyone is still out there fighting for their piece. We didn't even realize we were working together until we saw each other coming together side by side.

As for me, I have to keep my focus, and that is the health and well-being of the people. I look at that daily, weekly. I am thrilled with how the BLL's have gone down. But my focus is, whether people relocate or stay where they are, I need to make sure that they can be as healthy as they can where they are.

Yes, we all had different ideas. Yes, we all had disagreements. We didn't all agree on how we were coming together on things. But we all had one thing in mind from the very beginning: We are going to do this piece to the best of our ability. We want to fix this.

We'll wake up tomorrow, and we'll still be working on this.

"Lead Free the Bee, lead free is the way to be"—that became the motto of the Lead Prevention Program of the Ottawa County Health Department.

Photo courtesy LEAD Agency, Inc.

Photo courtesy TEAL archives

64

TRIBAL EFFORTS AGAINST LEAD

T.E.A.L.

Photo courtesy TEAL archives

It was a wonderful,
wonderful project.
It became a way of life.

Sally Whitecrow-Ollis
TEAL Clanmother Founder

I saw the job in the paper. I sent in my resume. They called me for an interview, and I went to Oklahoma City for the interview with Michelle, Bob and Lorraine, those three. I ultimately became the research assistant, but not in the beginning. When I went in, I was just looking for a job. But it kind of became a way of life. I loved all those people we worked with.

Michelle had given me some information on lay health advisors in other parts of the country and how they had dealt with breast cancer. I began to think about that and how we would deal with that as a tribe, about channeling the wisdom of the elders as lay health advisors. That is how that got started. I was thinking, as tribal people, who do we seek advice or help from?

We were just sure that this was something we had to do. But we were a little afraid, a little apprehensive, wondering how will we be perceived.

You don't want to offend people when you do something like this. I went and talked to elders because I wanted to make sure they wouldn't be offended if we used that name, the clanmothers. I had no intention of using *clanfather.* I didn't have men in mind at all since all the research was about breast cancer. It just worked out that men signed up, too. The men got into it quite well. It all seemed to fit, the kinds of people they wanted and the ones who could go out into the community, whether they met someone at the grocery store or at a family gathering. That was what we wanted. We wanted them to be able to tell those people a little bit. They didn't have to weigh them down with infor-

mation, just tell them a little bit each time to get them thinking. It worked out pretty well.

It was true in the beginning that no one wanted to hear about lead poisoning. I went to speak to the senior citizens because they asked me to speak. When I went in, when I walked up to the podium, I could already tell by all the grumbling. They said, "We have lived here all our lives and we have not been affected one bit by lead. My son went to college and graduated and we don't believe all this."

There went my prepared speech right out the door. Oh my gosh, what am I going to say to these people? I said, "You all know somebody who has high blood pressure, you all know someone who has died of cancer or heart attack." I was talking to elders, so I wanted to talk on their level. I said, "Lead poisoning can contribute to all of these things. We all know somebody who is a little dense, who we thought was just born that way. We all know those people. All of those things could have come about by lead poisoning."

That got their interest, and this one woman said, "My husband died of a heart attack a few years ago. I wonder, 'cause he had worked in the mines." We don't know, we will never know. It is a possibility that if he had not worked in the mines, he wouldn't have died that way. We could never say that for sure. It got them thinking that they could be affected and that their children could be affected. And their grandchildren. So it turned out to be a rather interesting conversation rather than a speech. That worked better. We just talked back and forth like a group, rather than me standing up and telling them things.

We just shared information. That is how the clanmothers and clanfathers were supposed to do: share information and pass it on. Like the little gossip game. You tell one, they pass it on. They all got it. At a party it never came out right, but this worked.

The woman who said that her son had graduated from college remembered, "We lived in Picher, but my mother was right there with a pan of water and soap waiting for us when we came home from school, and we all had to wash our hands." Her mother was a very smart woman. Then she in turn did that for her children. She hadn't thought to connect these actions until we talked about it, and then she could see the connection. She realized how it could have made the difference for her family.

We tried to recruit from every tribe and asked each tribe to recommend people who would be good clanmothers and clanfathers. We had a lot come in and out in the beginning. Some came to the training and did not continue with us. We had a good core group, and we developed our material ourselves.

They all had a different view—Bob Lynch was concerned about the contaminated soil, Michelle was more academic, Lorraine more scientific. We made a good team.

Our clanmothers and fathers learned things that they didn't think they would. I know I did. I didn't really know much about lead poisoning. I thought lead poisoning was if you stuck the lead of your pencil into your hand.

We also trained interviewers to go out into the community. Michelle, Lorraine and Bob developed the interview book for parents. It looked like a training manual. It covered questions about how children play and how often they wash their hands, if they live in a house that was built before 1978, if there are paint chips. It was a very in-depth interview about lead sources in the home.

Lorraine had maps for all the sections of each town. People went out and knocked on doors, using Lorraine's maps, and asked if the family had a child in that age group and if they would be willing to have their child's blood tested and do an interview. They would sign up, and we would send our interviewer out and a person to test the blood, a phlebotomist. They would do an hour-long interview, not trying to influence them with the interview, just finding out the family habits, to see what they did, so that if the child's blood was high, it would be easier to identify what was wrong and where the sources might be. They explained about nutrition using little plastic foods that showed portion sizes. The interview results were sent to Michelle.

We did some water sampling, leaving two containers with the family, asking them to collect the first water out of the faucet in the morning. Some samples were found to be pretty bad. Soil samples were taken at some houses; some homes were sampled for lead paint.

The first phase was getting the people to interview, then we did the interviews and got the blood samples and then, depending on the results, we would notify those parents what their child's blood lead levels were along with recommendations from the health department to find the sources. We did that in 2000 and again in 2002 and 2004. We did three screenings.

I think doing all these interviews and blood tests opened up a lot of eyes, because after that we began doing the trainings. We brought the head start and kindergarten teachers in for trainings. We tried to do daycare givers, though that was very difficult because they still had all their little children there. At least it was effective in teaching ways to prevent lead poisoning, like hand washing.

The clanmothers and fathers were the ones that did all the community efforts to spread the word about lead. We went in or set up booths at the county fair, all the powwows in the summer time, and all the tribal health fairs—and anywhere else there was something going on with the public.

Over and over again, the clanmothers and fathers have said they were really sorry it was over.

I think many learned things they didn't think they would. I know I did.

Photo courtesy TEAL archives

Cah-tee-lih Ollis in traditional Seneca clothing washes her hands.

Clanmothers and Clanfathers

Loraine Dixon	Kari Griffith
Virginia Fanning	Katie Birdsong
Patsy Henson	Marcine Quenzer
Flossie Mathews	Jack King
Barbara Mullin	Leonard "Catfish" Smith
Ardie Blair	Jesse McKibben
Helen Shamblin	Aline McNelis
Kyle Ollis	Sharon Burkeybile
Lorraine Young	Georgia Bear
Jay Whitecrow	Foxie Emerson
Bill Dixon	Fred Cata
Evelyn Bellmyer	Jennifer Lunsford
Coweta Ulrey	Joyce Perry
Mary Brewer "Mert"	Bill Perry
Rebecca Jim	Allen Perry
Pat Young	Karie Dawes
Kim Martinez	Kate Randall
Karen Fields	Kay Crow Ellison
Charla Gibson	Jamie Fanning
Dana Jim	Bill Bigheart
Anna McKibben	Juanita Bigheart
Glenna Wallace	Bobbie Munson
Beverly Farmer	Debbie Friend
Amanda Burleson	Melissa Jackson

Nature's harmful product
is still here.

Barbara Kyser Collier
TEAL Community Advisory Board Chair
Wyandotte Nation Environmental Director

I worked with the Wyandotte Nation in accounting and changed after the tribe started one of the first environmental departments. TEAL started after I was the environmental director for the Wyandotte Nation.

Initially, I was approached by Lorraine Malcoe and Michele Kegler. We tried to get representatives from each of the tribes to meet together and find out what kind of structure would be preferable for this community-based research project.

I was asked to be on the Community Advisory Board (CAB), because I was the oldest and had been around longer than anyone else. The CAB would be made up of a specified member from each of the tribes.

The CAB talked about the environmental and health issues, going way back when the acid mine water has been affecting everything—the downstream effects and how it was affecting each tribe's land base and what we could do about it.

One of the most interesting meetings was held at the Modoc Tribal Office when we decided on the name. We had a kind of contest. We chose TEAL because it was a word, then a logo—Tribal Efforts Against Lead. TEAL reached out to all the communities and tribal lands.

The clanmothers and fathers were created during Sally Whitecrow's reign. Each tribe was asked to send three members to be lay health advisors with a small stipend. All tribes participated initially.

Things have been tried—remediation, the buy-out. People say, they are just spending taxpayer money or it is just another government study. The land remediation, did it make it safer? Yes. Did it make it healthier? Yes. Will it stay that way? No, not unless they do something about the chat piles. I have nightmares about the chat piles.

I think other communities can profit from the documentation which gives a play-by-play account of the process of the TEAL organization and what was accomplished.

I feel the tribes and their contacts were of the utmost importance in this project from the beginning, and the groups formulated by the clanmothers and fathers and the youth throughout each organization were very productive, especially toward the blood lead issue.

Photo by Tina Smith

Kate Randall

Clanmother
Family Preservation Project Director
Wyandotte Nation

We can't destroy anything else
that we can't reclaim.

I was pretty excited to look back and realize what progress has been made since the TEAL Project was started in the area. When I joined the clanmothers, I felt like it was a grassroots group.

As Indian people, the environment is closest to our hearts. I'm not a biologist, I'm not a scientist, but I have a true love of Mother Nature and a true love of our people and a true love of what can happen to our land, both in the past and in the future. We are running out of land. We are running out of space.

I grew up in northeast Oklahoma and have been here all my life. The environment is the number one priority to me. Part of our environment we just accepted, like the lakes and streams and rivers. The chat piles were just hills to us. They were part of how people made their living at one time, and it was a part of our history and we really didn't see them as a threat—maybe an eyesore, but I never really thought they were dangerous.

When you went in that area, you were told to watch out for the mines, "Don't fall into the mines." People would go over there and drive their four-wheelers, and they would star gaze on top. There were no fences. They swam in the waters that were left behind. I remember as a teenager, I was told, "Go ahead and swim in the water. There are no snakes. Nothing can live in there." I don't know if that was true or not, but that was probably in the 1960s and early '70s.

I was really concerned about the area and protecting children so that was why I joined the clanmothers and fathers. Sally Whitecrow held a training class at the Modoc Tribal office

and may have had fifty people enrolled. The clanmothers and fathers went to powwows, downtown sidewalk sales and many community events. I remember going to the Picher Mining Days, the Ottawa County Fair, schools, and daycare centers. We passed out literature in every daycare center I can think of. No one was aware that a high blood lead level could cause such serious effects for children under seventy-two months old.

We had a lot of eyes to open right here. People at every educational level said, "I've grown up here and nothing's wrong with me!" I think some people still think that today, but not as many. It had to be proven to them, through testing and through the expertise of the doctors and scientists and environmentalists and everyone who came to look at our orange waters.

I work with Child Welfare for the Wyandotte Nation. At the last Oklahoma Indian Child Welfare Association meeting, Doug Journeycake took a very large group of people on what we call our toxic tour. We have educated other Indian nations, not necessarily the environmental departments because they already know, but everyone else who works in the Indian world with children. We have been doing this for the past decade.

My mother and I both were clanmothers. At first my mother was afraid to approach the general public. She was raised in a different generation, when women were not aggressive. She was native in her way to sit back and wait on someone to approach her. She would feel like she was pushing herself on other people. After she got over the initial shyness or her inability to speak in public, she really enjoyed the educational portion, the socialization in the community and especially in the Indian world. It was a real joy to her, and we spent a lot of time together on these projects. It was a way of bringing us closer. It was a great experience having my mom with us.

She really hated to see it end. We had a couple of pretty shy people who didn't like speaking in groups. Sally Whitecrow brought us together at pot luck dinner meetings and the fear lessened in a lot of our elders. She said, "It's OK to talk here, no matter what you say." I think Sally was really good about making us feel comfortable in that way.

We had three generations of people working as clanmothers and fathers, all with a passion for it, with Jennifer Lunsford and Kyle Ollis the youngest, in their early twenties. It was a great group of people. We made a lot of friends and we're still close today.

In the beginning when we passed out handouts, people didn't even know what we were talking about. You talk to someone today, there is no one in a hundred-mile radius that doesn't know what blood lead levels are, what the Tar Creek Superfund Site is. And now it could even be national and everyone will know about it. It has been one of the top ten toxic sites in the United States.

Working in Indian Child Welfare, I sometimes come home with a heavy heart. I come home and walk and get by the water. If we take away all of our peaceful environments, there will be nowhere to go to find your own peace.

The good that came from our work was awareness, not only for the people in our community, but I think this will eventually get out to the people in the world, what mankind can do to destroy the environment and how difficult it is to clean it back up or remediate it to what it once was.

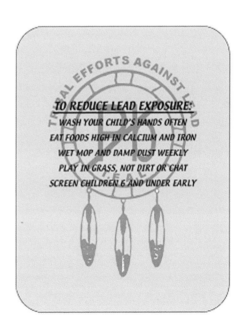

74

Photo by Tina Smith

Some people with big hearts went out
and gave everything they had.
They were the leaders and they had
a whole lot of followers.

Ardie Blair
Clanmother

A clanmother is normally an elder in the tribe. The tribes were separated by clans with names like Bird and Turtle. Clanmothers advised younger mothers about what to do when their children were sick.

Most clanmothers were older, grandparents. I was one of the youngest ones. I had young children when we began and another young woman had no children at all.

Here in Ottawa County we have a large number of children with high lead levels. Normally your lead level should be zero. You shouldn't have lead in your blood system. None of my children had high lead levels but I know other people who did.

As a clanmother with the TEAL Project, I would go into homes, powwows, health fairs. I would speak to people about how to keep their children from taking in so much lead.

Even though children are living in this, they don't have to have such high lead levels. Hand washing can help. Make sure children eat a healthy diet high in calcium and iron to help their bodies not uptake lead. Take off shoes when you come in the house, and keep outside toys outside. Make sure kids are doing all these things, and yes, that will limit their exposure.

Both EPA-remediated yards and awareness helped. Moving the contaminated dirt away from the kids was a good idea. The children's lead levels have dropped. It seemed to make a difference.

The tribes are sovereign nations and people forget that, but the tribes are nations within a nation. Or you could say it another way: The United States is a nation within our nations.

The Tar Creek Superfund Site sits right smack on top of the Quapaw tribe's original jurisdiction; the tribal members own 75% to 80% of the Superfund site. That was their original allotment land. Some land has been sold off, some taken out of trust. The Quapaw Tribe's environmental department has been pushing to do something since the very beginning. We fought the U.S. Government and I think we are on a winning streak. They are hauling the chat out but not quick enough to save the next generation. If they would shut the town down and move everyone out, if they chose to remediate the land to a native hay meadow and give it back to the Quapaw Indians, that would be a wonderful idea, too.

The credit for the success so far at Tar Creek has to be shared by a lot of different people, different organizations. The Quapaw Tribe all on its own didn't make this happen. Neither did the clanmothers and fathers or LEAD Agency. It's everyone combined. As a community, we came together, pushed for a remedy, pushed to make our lives better in Ottawa County. We have cared about each other, each other's families and each other's children. We have gotten to know each other. You don't see that a lot anymore.

Put the effort out there as a community, get all the resources together that you have, you can make a big difference.

Remembering ....

We had chat in our own backyard. My son's dog lived on it, that's where his doghouse was sitting. I didn't realize how much the small kids listen. Then one day my son asked me if his dog was going to die of lead poisoning. That's when I realized that the little bitty kids are the ones you need to teach. If you teach them, from that point on, as they have their own kids, they will know.

Lessons Learned....

I think that the biggest lesson that we can learn from this is, lots of times we sit back and see a problem and we think we can't do anything about it. "It's just me," we think, we can only teach our own children. But in reality, I taught a lot of other people's children. I spent a lot of time teaching people what I knew.

Glenna Wallace
Clanmother

I became a clanmother as an Eastern Shawnee. Our tribe is in the eastern edge of Ottawa County. Consequently we don't always get involved in all of the projects in the county. I was on the business committee, and once we heard about the TEAL project, we placed a couple of ads in our newsletter, *The Shooting Star*, but no one had volunteered to serve.

I did not want it to be said that the Eastern Shawnees did not have a representative. As busy as I was, I decided that I would be the representative; then I could tell others about it.

I learned a tremendous amount, and that education let me educate more adults than children. It has to be adults to teach the children. I was a college instructor at Crowder College at that time and taught speech classes. It could always be worked in as an informative or persuasive topic. So in telling my college students, some would pick those topics, meaning the education would reach 100 adults, not only in Ottawa County but in Jasper County, Missouri, and also from Kansas and Arkansas. Those students were just like I was. They were amazed that they had lived in this area and were not aware of this problem. It was a ripple effect. We were reaching far more people than we were aware of. I am sure every person in that group reached others.

When we first started as clanmothers, we had difficulty getting publicity or articles in the paper. If we went to a school and asked if the students wash their hands correctly, we were amazed to find out that most of the school districts didn't use hot water or even have hot water. So how can you teach them that you need warm water to wash your hands?

Today I look at the newspapers and see how much space is devoted to health and environmental information. I think this started with this group. This group was extremely instrumental. I feel we were the lead people to carry that message to the community. Action is taking place and this group mattered.

Many had to go through denial first and almost a refusal to believe to get to the point they are today. People have finally accepted the fact that yes, there was a danger, yes there is a danger, and yes we realize that we have exposed our children to this far longer than we should have. It's been an educational process—frustrating and now rewarding.

I was pleased when Eastern Shawnees Kim Martinez and Melissa Jackson became clanmothers. What pleased me more is that each of the tribes' environmental programs are stronger and larger, and we have become more aware and more diligent.

Lost Creek runs through our tribal lands and had become polluted; rather than letting it go, we made the effort to clean it up. And there are fish back in Lost Creek now. Not all of our tribal members understand why that was important. That is a battle we will have to continue, a battle of information that we have to fight. The clock is ticking now for Tar Creek, just how much longer will it take?

Remembering….

I remember being amazed at a daycare center in Picher when we offered a pottery class. The director was the parent of small children herself. She asked, "What do you people think of us who continue to live in Picher and who will not leave?" I was afraid to say what I really thought: How can you read this information and still talk today about chat pile riding yesterday with your children? How can you come in today with your children and hear the educational programs and choose to let it go in one ear and out the other? It is just astounding to me that when you don't want to believe something, you turn a deaf ear to it and do not believe it.

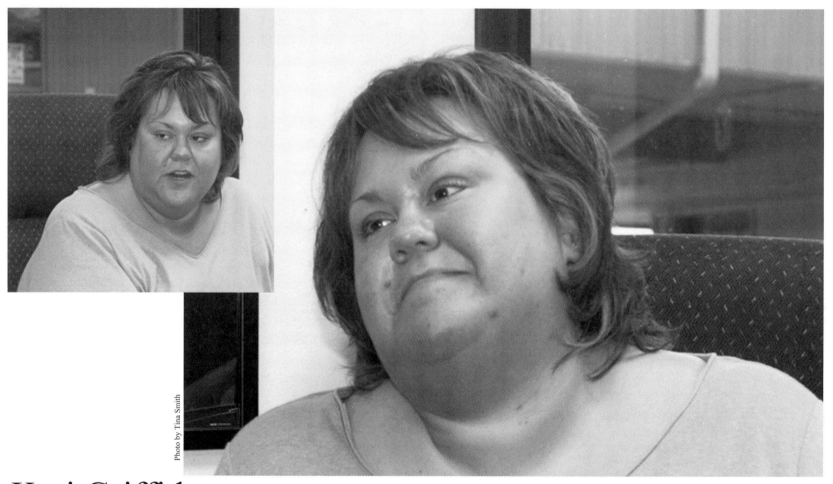

Photo by Tina Smith

Kari Griffith

Clanmother

Wyandotte Nation

You can feel the hopelessness.
That is what mining did.

I'm not the first generation to be in Ottawa County and not the last. My family goes back generations. I have a lot of family vested in this area. Yes, I'm passionate about what happens. Yes, I want to see it better. A lot of people working together can make a difference. I'm thinking about it from the standpoint of the kids that haven't been born yet.

I was a clanmother for the whole time there were clanmothers. We became a group of people who wanted to make a difference. The goal was to make a better place for the kids.

We were teaching. In the time I was with TEAL I saw people reach acceptance. Education brought that around. You have to understand that educating people in this area, you have to take baby steps. Because it wasn't like we woke up one day and boom, we have a problem. It's happened over decades. You can't teach someone about that in a year. People are learning. The true results are not here yet. When these children are parents, that is when we'll see if it is carried on to the next generation.

You go driving through there now, you can feel the desperation, you can feel the fear. Part of the fear comes from the education. You can't fear what you are not aware of. You can't fear what you don't know.

As we became more educated, the fear came.

Remembering....

I've seen Picher die. I've seen Tar Creek run clear to what it is now in my lifetime. I had an uncle who worked in the mines, so I got to see what his life was like after the mines. A lot of men had health issues. I've seen us not be able to swim and play in the creeks and streams in this area in my lifetime. Northeast Oklahoma is a wonderful place. I've never been anywhere else. But there is a sad aspect to it, too. You see the chat piles. Try explaining them to people who aren't from here: They are not mountains; they are hills of decay. The chat piles are what was underneath the ground; it's on top of the ground now.

I think of all the things we did as children, before we knew about the lead and the damage. When we were younger, we used to play on the chat piles. We used to swim in the sinkholes. We would eat wild asparagus that grows over there.

I remember driving through Picher when we were younger, seeing all the dust coming off the chat piles. We didn't have air conditioners in our cars. We didn't know we were breathing stuff that would kill us.

You go driving though there now, it's like driving through a ghost town. There is nothing there. It's pitiful, especially when you think Picher was going to be the county seat of Ottawa County. It had more people living there than Miami did. It used to be a happening place with a hospital, opera house and theaters. It used to have a trolley system that connected the three-state mining area.

Karen Fields
Clanmother

MATCH Project
Research Assistant

I don't want people to forget.
I want the work to go on.
I want people to keep trying
to find a solution to the problem.

82

Tar Creek is in an agricultural area. And we have Grand Lake. There is a lot of fishing that goes on. We have some industries around, but not a lot. We have a college and good school systems.

I know that people fish, and there is a limit to how many of the local fish should be eaten. Native Americans still pick berries and gather nuts to include in their diets. This is dangerous unless you know what you are doing. A lot of people eat wild mushrooms, like the morels. I for one do that and feel very comfortable eating them.

I think the local concern all started with Rebecca Jim. She has brought a lot of awareness to the community with her volunteer work with the Tar Creek Conference every year. The community comes out to it. She brought it out to the community, and I think it went farther than community. It's gone to the national level. She has had such a concern; she did not stop.

In some of the projects with TEAL I did with the clanmothers and fathers, we would go to Picher and meet with the students. They were so concerned about the lead issues in the area. One day, we divided up into groups and went to the businesses in Picher and posted the hand-washing stickers in each bathroom. It was neat to walk with five or six students down the street and go into each little business and ask to put the hand-washing sign in the bathrooms.

We also went into some homes to deliver HEPA vacuum cleaners for the parents to use. One mother said she would get up in the morning and send the children to school. "Then," she said, "I take my bucket and water and clean every single day, and when I dump the water, it is filthy. And I start over the next day. Where is the end? Will this ever end?"

It's been rewarding to me to be able to go out in the community to be able to talk to the mothers who have concerns about living in the area, to see that they are so concerned about their children, to go into the daycare programs and hear the day care workers be concerned about the children.

What I have learned about all of this is that the people are so caring and so concerned for the children in the area, and I just want it to continue. I don't want people to forget. I want the work to go on. I want people to keep trying to find a solution to the problem.

TO BEE GERM FREE & LEAD FREE... WASH YOUR HANDS!

A MESSAGE FROM THE OTTAWA COUNTY HEALTH DEPARTMENT, TRIBAL EFFORTS AGAINST LEAD (TEAL), AND L.E.A.D. AGENCY, INC.

It's a work of art by the community. Everyone has to help solve the problem.

Remembering....

The little convenience store south of Picher, no matter when you went in there, night or day, the shelves were always covered with lead dust. In 2000 you could see them dusting with a feather duster, but it was always there.

Working as a community health representative in 1971, I became aware of the danger of lead poisoning. They gave me free rein to start awareness about lead paint and the pottery from Mexico with beautiful designs full of lead. I began a campaign with the twenty-five community health representatives in our group, covering five counties. It was an eye opener.

The dust was the most contributive factor in my mind. We had a problem here. At that time people did not know what the lead content was in the air.

All the dust in the atmosphere became worse when there was a storm and heavy winds. Once I visited a friend's house in Cardin. When I walked in that table was clean. We had dinner, and when I left, I wrote my name in the dust all over the table. The fine dust would settle on there. That really told me that we had a problem deep down. There was nothing we could do about it back then. So it made me very aware of the problems facing people living in the areas of Picher, Cardin, and Treece.

We have a serious problem, and it's been kicked around and kicked around. Until someone takes a major step, I don't see any resolving it.

Photo by Tina Smith

Being a clanfather was an honor for me
—a great one.

Jesse McKibben
Clanfather
Former Chairman of the Quapaw Tribe
LEAD Agency

Remembering....

Starting in 1870, the Quapaw PowWow is the oldest in the nation. Scattered around the grounds are individual family camps that are used primarily in the summer. Beaver Creek runs through the site and has been the only way to cool down from the hot, humid Oklahoma summers.

We swam there until the creek was found to be contaminated with acid mine water and bacteria from illegal dumping of septic waste in abandoned mines. This also ruined the ground water. The tribe's environmental department created diversions for the public, providing misting tents to keep everyone out of the creek.

The grounds were covered with contaminated mine waste, used as gravel in the campsites. The grounds were cleaned up by the EPA but had to be corrected when it was found that the contractors had recontaminated the grounds with bad soil. It was brought out by "whistle blower" information.

Photo courtesy of Dobson Memorial Museum.

Gretchen Grotheer
TEAL Interviewer
Miami Tribal Environmental Office

When a parent, usually the mother, consented to having her child's blood taken, an interviewer would talk with her and ask questions in regards to their children's daily habits and activities, like how many times do they eat the same kinds of food a week and how often do they go outside to play, and do they wash their hands before and after they have meals and after coming in after outside playing?

On average the interviews lasted from forty-five minutes to one and a half hours. They were very specific. The researchers wanted the answers to be as detailed as possible about any kinds of activities at all having to do with chat. The people who came to take blood usually arrived around the middle of the interview, since taking blood didn't take that much time.

Besides conducting the interview, part of our job was to watch the blood-taking procedure, helping to keep the child calm. Both the parent and child were reassured that everything was legitimate and professional.

Usually only one child matched the criteria to be eligible for the blood draws. We had brochures and material to give out to parents interested in the home visits or in the main office. Our entire team tried to do twenty interviews a day in Miami, Picher, Cardin, Quapaw, Commerce and North Miami.

I will tell you right off, I'm not a people person. Given a choice I try not to work directly with the public. With this job it was a definite plus to be able to work with the public. I was happy to have stayed as long as I did. It changed me.

I am more tolerant of conditions and actually of people than before I took this job.

Kristen Thomas
2001-2005 TEAL Director

I was a transplant, I did not grow up here. It was a learning process for me, too. I think the gist of it is understanding the mining process. Seeing pictures before the chat piles had the biggest impact for me. Knowing that this area, Kansas and Oklahoma, was the plains, no trees, flat, just grass. Pictures before mining, that's the easiest way to explain it—to see then and see pictures now with chat piles. You think to yourself, Where did that come from? It came from underneath. It's such a fine material, fine small particles. The process it had to go through was amazing. Huge mountains— to think how much underneath the earth was torn up and processed in order to get the huge mountains. You think of the caverns and crevices that are under and are still a danger. Amazing. But you go to those same areas now, you can only see as far as the chat pile in front of you.

Ottawa County in northeast Oklahoma is a prideful area. The biggest challenge in my job was to find a way to tap into their pride. People thought we were spinning our wheels, but we were actually learning and getting to know the community and trying to get them on board with us.

Ottawa County will roll with the punches. They will find a way to adapt. There are lots of changes in northeast Oklahoma over the past 100 years even outside of the mining industry. This part of the country is very prideful in their roots. They pride themselves in being educated about what is going on and being survivors.

One of the things that meant the most to me was figuring out new ways to get people involved. The first five years of TEAL we focused, on educating parents and the adults. With the second TEAL, we carried that on, yet we focused on children. Educate the children, then they will educate their parents. That was amazing. Picher and Quapaw schools had projects. The children were empowered and they came up with their own ideas. They took off with ways to educate their community about lead poisoning. That was one of the most powerful education tools. The kids were raised in these communities. Their parents were from these communities. They went home and taught their moms how to clean and dust.

There was a shift. It was amazing to see.

Photo courtesy TEAL archives

Kristen Thomas took students to the Picher Mining Museum.

Pollution doesn't know
state boundaries.

Christen Creson Lee
TEAL Coordinator 2004 – 2006
Environmental Director
Wyandotte Nation

I worked with Emory University, getting in on the last couple of years of the TEAL project. It was fun and exciting and a learning experience for me. In 2004 we did the last round of blood lead screenings and the last of the educational activities.

I was new to the area, pretty fresh out of school. I had just graduated in 2003 from Missouri Southern University. It was the first time I'd ever seen the chat piles and learned about the lead problems and environmental factors.

Since then I've heard lots of stories about how the TEAL project impacted the community. I wish I had been part of it longer than I was.

Tar Creek was declared a superfund site the year I was born. When I first came here, there was a lot of communication with the big agencies: all the EPA operable units, the yard remediation and health studies and ecological studies. The population here doesn't know all the politics that have been played in the area. The agencies didn't talk to each other as they do now. The MOU (Memorandum of Understanding), the cooperative agreement, was signed the year I came, so that the states and the agencies would communicate with one another. The three states finally admitted that the Tar Creek site is a problem and is a part of the tri-state mining district.

Unfortunately, all of the pollution goes downstream. That is a big issue for the tribe I work with, the Wyandotte Nation. The downstream tribes were not included in some of the early discussions concerning what would be done. It is only in the past few years that we have been able to participate, reviewing documents and plans.

We are just now starting what EPA calls OU5. It's taken twenty years to get to this, finally realizing that there is something wrong with the drinking water, as well as the ground water. Besides the chat piles, there are other issues causing problems downstream. Are the fish safe to eat? Are the plants on the shore that we eat safe?

I was born in north Joplin, also a mining community. It also has the dangers of lead contamination, but not to the extent as here. As a new mother, I am concerned about the lead in the drinking water.

My husband Faron was born and raised in Picher, which is in the middle of the problem. He has seen a lot of things. We talk quite a bit about this. He comments, "This is a strong community. It's gone a long way. People have come to understand that there is a real problem with lead contamination here. They are concerned. The children are learning about the dangers."

We don't know how long it will take to contain the problem or if it can be contained. Education is the main factor in preventing any more contamination that results in health problems. Things will have to change until they can find a better solution.

Whether I am living here or somewhere else, there is pollution everywhere. Even if I lived south or north of here, metals contamination is not the only worry.

The agencies will probably be out of here in twenty years, but the small groups, non-profits, tribes, the environmental justice groups, the health department, they will remain. The

90

buy-out may happen over in Picher, but the tribes cannot go anywhere. They have jurisdictional lands; their people will be here forever.

I think that the agencies are working together to understand what is causing the pollution on a watershed approach across the three states. That has been the biggest help politically. They are all working together to understand what is causing the pollution. It is amazing how much is going on. The public has been able to get involved and make comments and lend their expertise to what is going on.

I wish I had been involved with TEAL in its prime. I hear stories of the clanmothers and clanfathers. I wish I had been here to see how they made a difference every day for over a decade. Our environmental department will continue the lead education as best we can. It is a sad thing to see TEAL end, but a lot of what the project did is being picked up by the health department, the Harvard study, and the other tribes.

Whatever we do today affects our children tomorrow.

Photo by Earl Dotter

Phillis Cruzan
Art Teacher Quapaw Schools
Parent

As a teacher I think everyone ought
to be thinking about the kids.

We did tons of things with TEAL.

TEAL helped us bring awareness that there are dangers out there and the possibilities of contaminants. They got us involved with so many things. They came and taught in my classroom about different problems we had with lead. They asked the kids what they thought they could do about it. The students made movies and had poster contests to do with the problems with lead and where it was, the big issues of the chat piles and living right in the middle of it and not thinking there was anything wrong with it. They learned more as they planned a bike ride, mapped the route and learned more local history. The Quapaw Tribe helped to give us their history and how the tribe fits into this area.

Looking back, I saw a lot of change in my students. Two elementary students won art contests with their posters, which were made into billboards. Now in high school, they are very proud of their part in making people more aware.

The chat piles were our landscape and certainly our recreation. Adults as well as children looked at them as a place to play. I even played on the chat piles as an adult, thinking more of the dangers to my body like broken bones. I didn't look at the inward damage I might be doing. As an adult, I thought I was okay with that, but when kids see adults play, they are going to do the same.

We brought to people's awareness that it looks perfectly safe to walk out across there, but there are hidden mine shafts, which are extremely dangerous. The chat piles have wooden towers in them, and they could impale you if you hit one.

Getting the word out about the hazard of play on the chat piles kept kids off private property and protected their lives. It made a difference.

The kids went to stores and put up the hand-washing stickers so they could feel like they were a part of something. Plus it was a reminder that no matter where we are on this earth, we need to take care of ourselves a little better. The stickers are still all over town.

We gave kids cameras with the instruction to capture pictures of dust. Of course, they took pictures of dust on TV's, but they went way beyond that. They showed how the dust settles on the grass beside the roads, where it is almost white from the dust. They looked everywhere, under things and on window sills. They even caught dust in the sunlight.

They thought of everything. They found it in their vehicles and in the mail boxes. Kids were amazed that their stuff was so dusty. We had a lot of fun with that and made collages out of the pictures. Since it was an assignment, they had to evaluate whether each was a good picture or a bad one. They put messages about dust on them like, "It's everywhere. You cannot get away from it. You can protect yourself from some of it, but some you cannot."

We had a variety of art projects, a little bit of everything. We integrated messages into whatever art concept I was teaching. We started incorporating graphic design with the computers, creating bookmarks and flyers. The kids kept coming up with ideas.

People learned that even the ground wasn't safe.

My kids still talk about their experiences. It got them out of Quapaw to work and interact with kids from other communities.

My students went on to address other issues, such as recycling, drinking, or being aware of how to protect yourself from the West Nile virus. It didn't always impact the ones who did the work, but it did impact the younger ones. We got a lot of things accomplished, and we had a lot of fun doing it.

I am sorry for people who are still in Picher, dug in, not going anywhere. If no one was there, the cleanup might go a lot faster. I don't want to see the demise of Picher, in any way. But I don't want to see the demise of our kids either. If walking across that ground is unsafe, and they could get hurt or killed, then they don't need to be there. If breathing that dust is the problem, then they don't need to be there either. As a parent, you had better think more about your children's lives because we are halfway through ours. We better start thinking about what our kids' lives are going to be like.

We did the right thing by teaching and educating people about these problems because education is the key to solving almost every problem we have. We taught older kids how to protect the younger children, whether it be their brothers or sisters or some other child in the community. No matter where we went, we taught something that was very good and beneficial.

Education is never wasted. It is the key to solving almost every problem there is. We educated the community and made the situation better. Did education stop that problem?

I can't say that it did, but I can say that no matter where we would have been, we helped prevent illnesses; even the common cold is passed along by not washing your hands. If contaminants are on your hands and you touch your food, you pass on those contaminants, whether it is a virus or lead or cadmium.

Remembering....

When I think about Picher, I do miss it because I lived in a neighborhood with friends right next door and couldn't walk outside the back door without saying hi. When I would see them doing something, I would go out and do it with them or just sit and visit. It was that type of friendly.

When my first neighbor moved away in the first buy-out, that was devastating. She was my best friend and her daughter was my daughter's best friend. That was heartbreaking. Then I moved away, too. I miss it terribly.

As a parent, you had better think more about your children's lives because we are halfway through ours.

Student posters were enlarged to become billboards in the communities.

Richard Zane Smith
Artist

We had a fun project funded by the Oklahoma Arts Foundation. I was asked to work with art students from each of the schools. I knew we only had a short period of time together. So I started thinking about Tar Creek and about what we could do with clay. Critters and clay? What could a kid come up with ? A fish? A fish that had been polluted.

The ideas were going around in my mind. The kids are going to like this idea. We got there, got the clay, and said, "We are going to make fish that come out of Tar Creek." These had to be weird fish, strange fish. Their eyes started lighting up. That is what they made. There were fish with frog legs and fish with worms coming out of them. The students went to the art studio to finish the fish, allowing them to see what an artist studio looked like.

The project was a political statement. At the Tar Creek Conference, each fish was placed at the meal table with a place setting. There were no words displayed. No one ate one. Not a bite out of a one.

We've pulled all of the minerals out of the land, and money was made. But no one thought about the future generations, like the native way of thinking. We are always thinking of at least to the seventh generation. Thinking of the effects.

Photo courtesy LEAD Agency, Inc. archives

We've pulled all of the minerals out of
the land, and money was made.
No one was thinking the native way,
of the seven generations to come

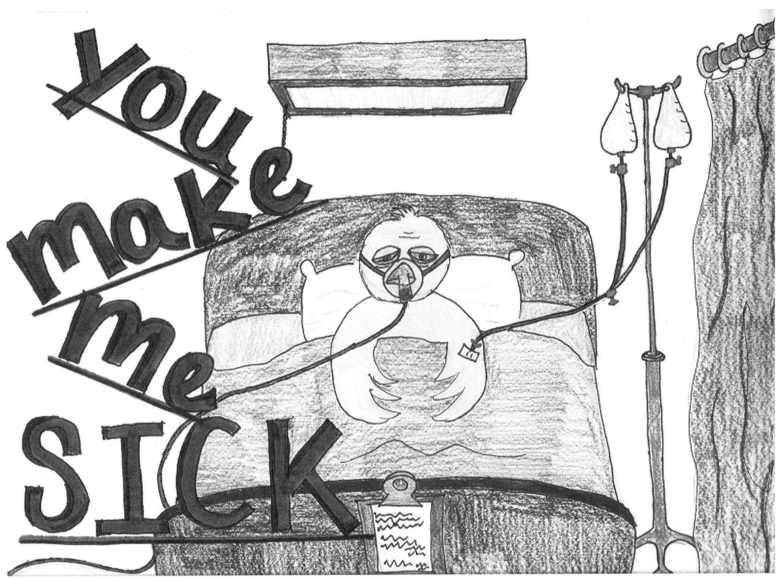

Poster by: Jacque Matthews

Student posters and their written work help give youth voice to the issues they face.

Mike McAteer

EPA—Region 6
Remedial Project Manager
Operable Unit 2 Residential Yards

A lot of community people have stayed on top of EPA. This has led us.

I've been with EPA for over sixteen years in the Superfund division, with the first eleven years in the Chicago office. I was at a conference once with a lot of project leaders of Superfund projects from around the country and saw a presentation on Tar Creek. I was impressed with everything going on here, the scope of the problems. Then by coincidence in 2001, I transferred to the Dallas office and not long after that began working on the Tar Creek site. I heard about Tar Creek years before actually coming.

When I first came, I was overwhelmed. My reaction was, "Wow, this is a lot to take on." We know how to clean up yards, but everything that goes on around them and surrounding the yards took my breath away at first.

EPA's yard removal action, OU2 started because someone brought it to us. The Indian Health Service had data that showed children had elevated blood lead levels. They asked, Did you all know about this? We didn't know. They raised the issue. And I am glad to say that we were able to take it seriously.

My role with EPA at Tar Creek for the past five years has been to work on residential properties. There is nothing quite like being in somebody's backyard. Not everyone was happy with us. The good news is that the yard remediation worked and the outreach education program worked. The blood lead levels of children are down to state and national averages. That's a big success and we are happy about that. We did something to improve the lives of children. I sleep better at night because this really made a difference.

This is obviously a unique site with so many aspects and so many people affected. There are so many issues. It's ground water. It's surface water. It's soil. It's air, it's everything. There aren't enough resources to go around to do this all at once. We have to break this into pieces and do each as quickly as we can.

At most Superfund sites, you don't get results. In a lot of sites, we take action and spend taxpayer dollars based on potential risk. It's all on paper and no measurement afterwards. But this was a site where children had already been put at risk and harmed. Here now, the risk is gone. We were able through a concerted effort with the health department, LEAD Agency, the tribes and others, to get blood lead levels down. It's not zero, so I'm not happy about that. But we protected kids. We made a big improvement.

I think that is what has happened, by staying with it, keeping everyone involved and letting people, not just the federal government, the tribes, the county, obviously, the residents most affected and academia, doing some of the work, not waiting for the federal government. We never saw a community group like LEAD Agency get that involved and take on as much as they have taken on.

The fact that we are going into the next phases honestly has a lot to do with the community staying on top of it. I have seen the willingness to keep working with us and keep us focused on what needs to be done, the concerns of the people who actually live here. That is why it is a success.

Lessons Learned....

There are lots of lessons learned at a site like this. Counterparts in other areas don't do things like we do, but there are a lot of things they see that we are doing and say, "Hey, maybe we could do something different like that." Everyone has worked together, and I don't mean that with rose-colored glasses. It really has been unique. There is a lot of learning from that. That has been a positive in this whole thing.

I think the biggest lesson-for us at EPA is that it's a good thing that everyone be involved, and I don't mean giving lip service but actually getting involved.

We got this far with persistence, by not giving up.

Rafael Casanova

EPA—Region 6
Remedial Project Manager
Operable Unit 2 Residential Yards

I really enjoyed doing the work. I enjoyed working with the tribes and the Hispanic population. I enjoyed the fact that we were doing something good.

EPA sampled the yards and found high lead contamination, which was a risk to human health. The target population was the children under six because their normal hand-to-mouth activities exposed them to lead, would enter their blood systems. That was the concern. From the study they did, we knew we had high lead levels in children. So we had to do the cleanup.

I was a remedial project manager, responsible for oversight of the cleanup. When I came, the removal action had just started, working on residential yards. EPA oversaw the Army Corps of Engineers, which was the prime contractor, with the subcontractor, Morris and Knutson.

We had community meetings and did as much as we could to inform the community about the contamination at the site. We met with state, county, city, tribes, and worked as best we could with so many people involved. For me it was almost overwhelming. We met with the mayors monthly from the five cities—Picher, Cardin, Commerce, Quapaw and North Miami—to report on what we had done and answer concerns.

As far as the relationship between the tribes and myself, we had no conflicts at all. I tried to work with them as best I could. I would get a call, "Can you help me this weekend? Can you give a talk to the tribal elders?" And I would do it. Whatever they needed, I would do.

I saw a need to target the large Hispanic population, and I visited a lot of them. Since I spoke and wrote Spanish, I could write the fact sheets in Spanish. I visited churches and did a lot of presentations in Spanish. I tried to do as many as I could. At the request of Susan Waldron, I went to a school and did a presentation in Spanish to pregnant women to educate the mothers on the effects of lead. I talked about lead and gave a history of the site. I talked about the effects of lead on young children and how to prevent lead exposure, mostly by good hygiene. I was surprised to learn that a lot of the Spanish community did not know about lead at the site. They would say, "This is here?" I was really surprised to know that they did not know that there was a possibility of lead exposure here. They saw the chat piles, but they had no idea what was in them. They were surprised to learn about the mining.

I went to a Cinco de Mayo fair and spoke, impromptu, initially with Susan Waldron. She had a van for lead testing there.

After that, I did work a lot with the county health department and the van. We would park at WALMART. Susan made a deal with Pizza Hut. She encouraged people to get their children tested for lead by giving out certificates for medium pizzas. When people would walk into the store, I would target the Hispanic families, run over and offer free pizza. "Want to get blood lead tested?" That was a way we got a lot of them.

Our contractor and I went to all the elementary schools and did presentations for all the kids. We spoke mostly about safety concerns because we had heavy equipment at the school. But we also talked about lead poisoning. We did that two years in a row. We targeted mostly kindergartens.

Now, I am doing cleanup in Houston. It involves a yard remediation for a foundry two miles from downtown Houston. It is a lead site, and so I am still doing lead cleanup. All the work that we did at Tar Creek, we carried it forward to Houston. We are doing it the same way with the same procedure.

I enjoyed working with the people there at the site; the mayors were very interesting, and I enjoyed working with the tribes.

Remembering....

We went to career day in Picher and talked to about a hundred kids. They asked, "What does it do to us? How can we avoid it?" Many students knew a lot about the mining. In Picher in the cafeteria, you can see a big mural of the mines. Many of the younger students didn't know about the lead. I answered many questions about flotation ponds. We talked about the fine sand at what's known as the "beach" area. Many kids were surprised to know that the sands were part of the mining process. One boy came up after the talk and said that he and his friends go out there all the time. I told him that they shouldn't do that because the fine sands are really high in lead.

Lessons Learned....

When I was at Tar Creek, I was a member of the lead sites work group. We wrote a handbook about how to do residential lead cleanup and investigation. Now that handbook is the national guidance on lead sites all over the nation.

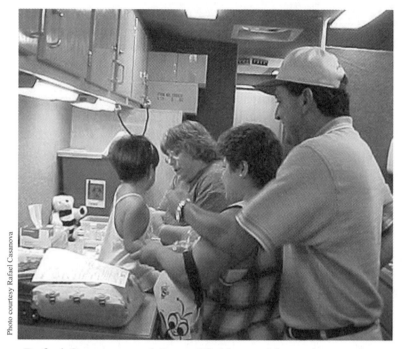

Rafael Casanova and Susan Waldron with a parent and child in the hospital's mobile unit.

I could see that we were
actually getting something done.
It's all education. It's all cleanup.
And it is a lot of work.

EPA removed soil contaminated with lead from residential yards and places children play

Jennifer Lyke
ATSDR Representative
Region 6

I became involved with Tar Creek in 1993 when ATSDR was beginning a Site Review and Update for the Tar Creek site. I came back to the office telling my boss he'd never believe the size of these piles.

Soon after, I began working with the County Health Department and the Indian Health Service clinic. The commitment of these two groups was unbelievable. As EPA began evaluating the risk of the chat, these groups really mobilized and committed to health education. After working with EPA during their evaluation of the high access areas, ATSDR was approached to provide oversight of blood lead screening and health education activities. EPA was willing to provide the funds if ATSDR would, in turn, provide the funds to the Oklahoma State Department of Health/Ottawa County Health Department and provide the oversight of these activities. The dedication of the OCHD staff to conduct these activities was truly monumental.

Working with the tribes has opened my eyes to many cultures that I hadn't experienced previously.

The one thing that draws me, though, is the people and their love for each other and their community.

The Agency for Toxic Substances and Disease Registry Response for Children at the Tar Creek Superfund Site

ATSDR-sponsored activities have helped produce a significant drop in blood lead levels (BLLs) among young children in Tar Creek. In 1996, Oklahoma State Department of Health (OSDH) data showed that among young children (aged 1-5 years) living at the site, 31.2% had a BLL at or above 10 micrograms per deciliter (μg/dL), the CDC level of health concern. By 2003, OSDH data indicated that elevated BLLs among children in the same age group had dropped to just 2.8%.

ATSDR is based in Atlanta, Georgia. It is a federal public health agency of the U.S. Department of Health and Human Services. ATSDR was created by the Comprehensive Environmental Response, Compensation, and Liability Act of 1980 (CERCLA), more commonly known as the Superfund law. The Superfund program is charged with finding and cleaning up the most dangerous hazardous waste sites in the country. ATSDR supports this mission by providing and using the best science, taking responsive public health actions, and providing trusted health information to prevent harmful exposures and disease related to toxic substances. Statistics reported in October 2004 to Congress by the Agency for Toxic Substances and Disease Registry (ATSDR) show that in 1996, approximately 31.2% of the children aged 1-5 years living in Tar Creek had elevated blood lead levels.

As of 2003, the average blood lead level and the percentage of elevated blood lead levels (those greater than or equal to 10 ug/dL) had decreased from 31.2% to 2.8%. Therefore, the average blood lead level and the percentage of elevated blood lead levels among children tested for lead who lived in the Tar Creek area were only slightly higher than for all children tested in the United States during 1999-2000. The following graphs illustrate this decline in blood lead levels at the Tar Creek Superfund Site.

Children's Blood Lead Levels (ATSDR)

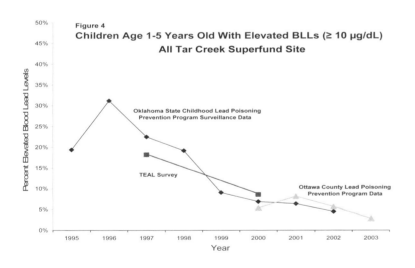

Children's Blood Lead Levels (ATSDR)

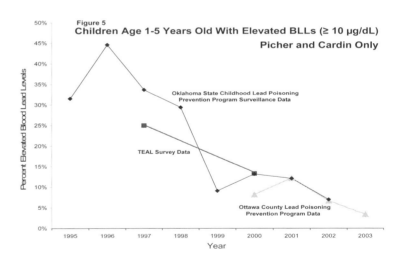

Photo by Tina Smith

Tami McKeon
Lead-Based Paint Abatement
Grand Gateway

It wasn't always easy.
There were discouraging moments.

We might not all agree on how to get there, but we all know where we need to go, and that is to make this a safe place for the children.

While I worked with Grand Gateway, a council of governments, I was in charge of a HUD Lead-Based Paint Abatement Program in the Picher and Tar Creek area. We ended up doing a total of fifty-one homes with the first grant funding, assessing each home with children under six years old and checking the painted surfaces for any lead-based paint.

We had a successful program, and we applied for a second set of funding and were successful in that as well. We had hoped to get 150, but we ended up going into 124 homes and abating all of the lead-based paint issues out of those homes. That involved going in and testing for lead-based paint and having the children tested for lead at the health department or Indian Health Services or with their own private physician. We fixed the lead-based paint by various methods. We relocated the families to a safe environment while work was being done, and then we moved them back. So it was a very complex job with many different tasks to work on.

There were many single-parent homes, headed up by grandmothers or great aunts. We reached out to the grandmothers when they were taking care of children during the day. Then we went back and helped the moms in their own homes. We got a lot of referrals that way. We were successful in taking care of those families.

We had three lead-safe homes that we rented for families to stay in so that the children could continue to go to their own schools and continue in the lifestyle that was familiar. The houses weren't mansions by any stretch of imagination but were fully furnished with dishes, linens, an ironing board and washer and drier. They had all the amenities you would have at home. This way they didn't have the costs of having to eat out three meals a day. All they had to move were their clothes and the baby's food and bottles. The goal was to have the three houses full, but that didn't always work out.

Just the sheer time line issue of getting people in and out, the contractors in and out, and making everyone happy all at once could be very stressful at times. And you have no control over weather. The paint encapsulant had to be applied on days when it was 50 degrees or warmer.

As far as the local support, it couldn't have been better. LEAD Agency, the Cherokee Volunteer Society, the health department, and the schools let us do a lot of outreach activities. We also provided education to the families while they were in relocation so they didn't just go back in and have nothing to work with. They needed to know what to do in case they ever moved into a different home that had the same sorts of issues.

You know I am a strong faithful woman. I feel like a lot of this work is part of my mission. I think everyone needs to believe in something. If they don't, how can they find the right direction?

I know that there are other beliefs, and I respect that people have those.   If we serve the earth, it obviously comes back to serve us. Sometimes we get that a little backward and disrespect her; that is a shame. We had better respect her, or she will come back and slap us.

I am really pleased at the way everyone has worked together, through thick and thin, and there have been thick times and thin times.

It would be a proud legacy to leave our children with a clean creek and restore the lands back the way they belong. I have come to appreciate that more, after working with a tribe. It's been very enlightening to realize and appreciate the stance of different tribal governments and their relationships with the earth.

Remembering ....

The most memorable case that we had was with a three-year-old child who had an elevated blood level. We were standing out on the porch, and that child had a habit of twirling himself around the porch post. When I saw him with that post, I just knew that was the problem. And lo and behold, that was the culprit. We fixed the porch post, as well as all the other lead-based paint surfaces in the home, and there was a remarkable and significant difference in his blood lead level—snap—just that fast. It really just moves your heart to know that you made a difference in that child's life. He had so many other strikes against him; the very last thing he needed was lead poisoning on top of everything else. The home was very humble. They had no money and no resources. They were so grateful that the grandmother had tears in her eyes. It was very moving to be able to reach out and help those people. I really think that this has had a significant impact in his life. It really compelled me to keep on going.

Photo by Tina Smith

Diane Bostic
Clinical Coordinator
NEAHEC

When I think about the situation here, I see how greed is at the bottom of it. It violates all of nature, human nature. Greed is the core. The people who profited from the mines didn't take care of it then and are not taking care of it now.

I am a Quaker and Jennifer Caron is a Quaker and she got to Tar Creek through her meeting and stayed for a summer as a Quaker Witness. She spent a bit of time in Tulsa with a Quaker family and that family invited Jennifer and Rebecca and her mother to an information meeting that our meeting sponsored. Not many people came. It was just talking, casual, in a circle. That's how I learned about Tar Creek.

I've worked for over ten years with Anne Wilson Schaff who is Cherokee Indian—and had been taught about honoring the land and caring for the land. It was just imperative to me personally to get involved. I had to ask, What can I do? How can I participate?

My part is to work with current health care professional students and give them meaningful experiences. I also got the Rural Health Department at the College of Osteopathic Medicine to create a Tar Creek Superfund Site medical elective, which has struggled, because we don't have a clinical experience to be in tandem with it. So we have had only two or three students. But four times a year, I have four medical students here with local doctors and all are required to go on the toxic tour and to hear about the health implications.

I also work with nursing students. The Oral Roberts University nursing students come in the fall and in the spring to do a number of different projects. They helped with LEAD Agency's Environmental Justice lay health survey.

One semester I worked with Oklahoma University graduate nursing students immediately following the health survey. They crunched numbers and did the comparisons with the national standards and state standards for all of the health issues. They presented the results at the National Conference on Tar Creek and then many knowledgeable researchers in the field questioned this highly touted lay survey, its validity, its efficacy. There was even pressure at the University of Oklahoma about funding. But that was a number of years ago, before the first buy-out, before people were embracing this as the right thing to do, when there was a great deal of denial. That was the political climate.

I've just been a broker. I go on a lot of the tours. Every year I bring forty undergraduate nursing students on tour. The experience is different each time, bringing students and creating awareness in people who have lived in Tulsa all their lives, even connecting the local physician. He'd been here five years and never been out there. We put him in the van and he just went into a state of shock. He kept saying, "Unbelievable, unbelievable."

What is happening here is a community empowerment model.

About the Northeast Area Health Education Center

The Northeast Area Health Education Center (NEAHEC) is a state and federally funded agency with a mission to alleviate health care shortages in the rural and urban underserved areas. It has facilitated hundreds of health professional students touring and learning about the effects of the Tar Creek Superfund Site upon the environment and the health of area residents. Oklahoma State University Center for Health Sciences (OSUCHS) offered a Tar Creek elective allowing medical students to study the issues more fully while rotating with Dr. Duane Koehler in Miami, Oklahoma. All OSUCHS Rural Clinic medical students rotating in this area have spent a half day hiking in the area, getting a first-hand look at the magnitude of the environmental problems and the health implications. Health care professional student rotations, facilitated by Dianne Bostic, NEAHEC Clinical Coordinator and LEAD Agency, include OU-Tulsa BSN, OU MSN, and Oral Roberts University (ORU) BSN Students. In addition, ORU BSN students have worked in the Miami and Picher communities facilitating public health surveys, working in the Community Free Clinic, and supporting healthy life styles in collaboration with the Miami schools.

Kendra Jezek PhD, RN
Dean
Anna Vaughn School of Nursing
Oral Roberts University

I am pleased that our nursing students had the opportunity of working in the Tar Creek community. I believe that exposure to a broad range of experiences reflecting the "human condition" is essential to nursing education. Because Oral Roberts University is situated in Tulsa, our students have many experiences in major urban hospitals and even community agencies. I wanted our students to have experiences in rural settings directed at nursing care for the community as client.

Upon touring the community, I was convinced that students would have a rare and special experience. I'll never forget my short hike with Rebecca Jim to a polluted swimming hole and posting the "No Swimming" sign, the huge chat piles everywhere, the emerging sink holes with rusty water bubbling to the surface, and actually meeting Bobby Kennedy, Jr., at the source of the obviously polluted Tar Creek! I was alarmed that residents actually swam in the polluted sinkholes and rode motorcycles across the chat piles, seemingly ignoring the danger that seemed so obvious. I vividly recall Rebecca's stories of school children who, because of the lead poisoning, experienced learning difficulties and be-havioral problems, with many dropping out of school. Her passion about the people and her determination and persistence to help her community were contagious. By the end of the day, I knew this was an experience I wanted our students to have.

I knew there would be challenges convincing faculty to take on this assignment, for a number of reasons: It was innovative and outside our comfort zone, it required a long commute that would lengthen the clinical day by at least three hours, and travel expenses would have to be funded.

Although faculty was initially reluctant to accept the challenges and students complained about the long commute, all wholeheartedly embraced the experience. We secured a university van for travel, and NEAHEC, with whom we partnered for the experience, provided travel funds. Faculty and students utilized travel time for pertinent discussions and accomplished much work during this time. Students truly addressed community as client, working with LEAD Agency, the local health department, and public schools. In fact, the experiences were so successful that faculty soon believed that it was their idea!

The experience gave students a rare opportunity to view the community as client and to work collaboratively with a variety of persons from various community agencies. Certainly, the students' experiences exceeded my expectations!

Laurie E. Doerner RN, MSN
Instructor of Nursing
Oral Roberts University
Anna Vaughn School of Nursing

My first memories of Tar Creek are hearing about it as a Superfund site when Mike Synar was the congressional representative for that district. My reaction was probably pretty typical: I thought it was bad for the people who lived there and was glad to hear that the government was working to clean it up. I heard about it periodically when I listened to the news but just tucked the information away in my memory. After all, I wasn't personally impacted.

Then I met Rebecca Jim in the summer of 2003. Dr. Kenda Jezek (Dean of the Oral Roberts University Anna Vaughn School of Nursing), Audrey Thompson (ORU nursing faculty), Dianne Bostic (NEOKAHEC) and I (ORU nursing faculty) took the Toxic Tour with Rebecca. I laugh now because I showed up in my cute black linen mules and cropped pants thinking I was going for a nice drive in the country. Needless to say, we drove through Commerce, Picher, Cardin, Douthitt, and all. We hiked back into a lovely blue-green water-filled sink hole, where people love to swim, in Kansas over a rocky, dusty berm. We drove past the mountains of northeast Oklahoma (aka chat piles) and listened to Tar Creek as it bubbled and tinkled under the Douthitt bridge, turning orange as it flowed toward Grand Lake.

In the fall of 2003, I began bringing seniors from the school of nursing to the area. We have worked with LEAD Agency since 2003 to teach children about protecting themselves from lead. We've interviewed tribal members about their health as part of an environmental impact study, participated in fund-raising activities to support lead prevention education programs, collaborated with high school students in a schoolwide assembly about the dangers of drug use, and collaborated with art students to create lead exposure prevention educational materials for community education projects. A poster created by the students the first year we came is now a billboard on Steve Owens Boulevard. Hopefully it makes every driver who sees it think about the impact of heavy metal contamination on themselves and their children.

I've been amazed by the progress to eliminate chat piles and fill in sink holes that present multiple health hazards to the community. Students are always amazed by the poverty, hopelessness and environmental devastation

My students and I see that the efforts of people in the community make a difference in the lives of people who live here.

Tamera Summerfield
Deputy Tribal Administrator
Lead Impacted Community Relocation Trust

Quapaw Tribe Secretary/Treasurer
Former Quapaw Tribal Chair
First and Second Buy-Outs

I have served as a volunteer on the Lead Impacted Community Relocation Trust for the first and second buy-outs of residents in the Tar Creek Superfund Site. Nine people were appointed for the trust by Governor Henry—a wide variety of people like bankers and lawyers, and other people. The Trust will continue until the money runs out.

I think getting the people out of the most dangerous area is a good thing. I was on the Trust earlier for the buy-out for families with children aged six and under. Fifty-five families were involved in that. It was cut and dried. That buy-out had to do with the lead contamination.

The second buy-out came about because of the subsidence report, so many more people were involved in this buy-out. There were hundreds of applications this time around, and there is not enough funding to buy-out everyone. It is so much more involved with the businesses and people who own empty lots or farm land. That is why we have gone through the process of prioritizing locations by risk of collapse and going down from there to the elderly and disabled.

I observed at the first meeting that everyone was really nice and friendly, agreeing that we need to get the elders out first, but now you can see it slowly dividing the community. You see a group here, a group there. The good part is that people are going to get to move out of there. The bad part is that it has torn up the community. You have people saying, "Why is he getting out? He isn't disabled." People forget that this buy-out is for safety. There have been a lot of complaints, but no one has turned down an offer. All those offers that have been given were accepted.

We are working with the cities of Picher and Cardin on what will happen to the people who don't want to go and who we don't have the money to buy-out. The cities won't have infrastructure with utilities. How are we going to help these communities survive because they are not going to go away completely. That is something we are still struggling with.

Most of the impacted land is not owned by the tribe. The land is owned by individual tribal members because of the Allotment Act before statehood. The tribe itself has a very small interest, but with tribal members, land is part of our tribal land base. We have some authority. Probably 40% to 50% of the affected land is Indian trust land.

What we are hopeful for and pushing for is to have the land acquired by the Trust be turned over to the tribe to manage. What we would like to see is something similar to what Governor Keating tried to do with the wetlands, but on a smaller scale. We want to make something good there. I don't think it would be wise for people to live here. I think if some of the areas are collapsed, and they are filled with water, that is one of the possibilities. We don't want tall fences around chat piles scattered all over our lands. The Quapaw Tribe can turn the land into something that looks better and isn't dangerous for people to live near or drive through. That is what we would like to see.

My family lives in Miami. My son is now thirteen years old. I had his blood tested for lead when he was young. It was a little elevated, and he was diagnosed with ADHD and some hearing loss in one ear. He had some symptoms that are associated with elevated blood lead levels. We lived in Quapaw when he was found to be lead poisoned and that did scare me. My kids are pretty familiar with chat because of the outreach in school, and my husband is always talking about environmental issues. They may know more than most kids.

Living in Miami, I am sure there is chat all over the place. I think we are ignorant, thinking since we live over there that it is not a problem with the environment or the health risk. We are affected, even the economic part of it. I think that having a Superfund site is part of our economic condition because people hear about the horrors of Tar Creek, and who wants to move here with their kids or open a business? It is real and it is true.

I think the tribe could get a handle on this. I don't think the state wants to deal with it. I think if the state gets those lands, they will just fence it. If we get it, we could get federal trust and federal oversight of it and take it a little more seriously. The state doesn't want to put the money into it. The Trust will be the owner of the land acquired in the buy-out and will make the decision about what to do with it. Everybody agrees that since it was formerly Quapaw land, if the tribe is willing to take it, why not give it back. I don't know how the people left in the community would feel about that.

The buy-out is creating a lot of problems, but making people safe is a good thing. I don't know if it is better in all respects. Some things are getting worse, creating the problem with the school, the city government, and the ambulance service. The tribe is trying to pick up some of these services. These issues make it difficult. It makes it tough

Kids are going to be safer.

117

KIM PACE
Principal
Picher Elementary School

Before I became a principal, I was a regular K–12 teacher, a special education teacher, and a teacher for children with learning disabilities.

When I look back over my career and my undergraduate work, what I noticed was that a large percentage of our children had attention deficit disorder. We just didn't know to call it that then.

These children could not attend. If someone coughed, they looked. If someone got up to sharpen a pencil, they were totally distracted. We made up for that by covering the windows and blinds. We had specific skill packets and helped these students with their particular needs—processing, discrimination problems, auditory, and visual. We determined the need through testing, then we taught to that particular disability.

In 1989 I became the elementary principal. Having that knowledge, we were identifying fifteen to twenty kids a year with learning disabilities. If a child can't read, the automatic assumption is that they ought to be in a special education classroom. In my beginning years, I just had any child who was struggling in the classroom, from kindergarten through twelfth grade. It was the most painful thing to watch children who could not read. They could not read. It didn't matter what kind of reward we gave them.

When we started to figure out that these children were having such difficulty learning to read, we had to do something different. I also saw sixth graders hit the wall with math, transitioning to abstractions, formulas, and beginning algebra. It wasn't until 1994 that I started thinking that what they needed were more repetitions.

I started doing a longitudinal study of our children because I wanted to know how long the children with learning disabilities stayed in our school system. Out of thirty-five seniors, only five had started and stayed in Picher schools. That makes a difference. There were lots of changes at that time. BF Goodrich and Yellow Transit closed down, and people started leaving. People moved in who were hiding or running from something, and so we had five to seven years of lots of mobility.

My little brother went through some difficulties in learning to read. We had taken him to Tulsa for vision therapy. They taught us how to do the eye exercises he needed to help him work his eyes together. I can't prove that exposure to lead caused this problem.

When EPA got back here, Northeastern State University decided to come in. Dr. Jack Davis of the College of Optometry and Dr. Karen Cornell did neurocognitive tests on children with high blood lead levels, whose parents would allow it. They did an acuity test and the vision therapy test on every child. Then when the first law suit was filed, those stats were locked up in a file in a statistician's office in North Carolina. So that information I have never had. Dr. Davis said, "Kim, 90% of your kids are having trouble with vision therapy. You have maybe ten students who need glasses, but out of 256, the majority of the students have vision therapy problems." Many of our children's eyes were not working together.

We started using reading helpers, color-coded transparencies, and we started to see some change in our kids. They could read. They would say, "The letters are not jumping around anymore."

In 1997 I heard about Literacy First, an innovative approach to teaching reading. When we started Literacy First, 23% of our kids were reading on grade level. A regular student would take fourteen repetitions, but our kids would take seventy-five repetitions to obtain that same skill. We have seen phenomenal success with these new techniques. Literacy First is the great equalizer. It did for our kids what the typical reading teacher could never have done.

I've found that you view yourself as a reader in the same way you view yourself as a person. Self-esteem is so interwoven and interrelated with it that if you don't view yourself as a good reader, then you view yourself as dumb and stupid.

At the same time we were doing all this, we were also embracing a behavior-teaching approach called Great Expectations, and it filled in all the gaps and did for children's self -esteem what needed to happen. They started to experience success. The reading levels went from 23% to 87%.

Once they could read, everything fell into place. They had confidence to try new things. And we had a mission. We had consistency. We had a goal. My job was to bring this approach to the teachers; the teachers' job was to bring it to the babies. The children's jobs were to work their brains out so we could see success. And now we have a literate community. My dream for these children has come to pass. It is a reality.

If there's anything that we know for sure, it is that any amount of lead is not good. It doesn't matter how much. We know that for a fact, and so let's try to clean it up. Obviously, we have made attempts. We have made some progress, but we are not going to live long enough for this to be cleaned up in our lifetime.

Note: Literacy First is a research-based reading reform process for students in grades Pre K-12. Principal's instructional leadership role is strengthened. Teacher instructional skills on the reading process refined.

Note: Great Expectations is a school reform model based on research and "best practices" in education and youth development. The training aids teachers in working within their curriculum areas to meet the needs of students.

Remembering….

I had waited my whole life to be twenty-five. I thought by then you would probably have your college education, a little bit of wisdom, and probably were thinking about getting married and starting a family. With my daughter Kylee, I worked backward. If that is the age I always wanted to be, what would it take to make her a happy, successful twenty-five-year-old? With that thought in mind, I worked backwards to birth and the milestones per year. What should I be exposing her to all the way through? That was my theory.

I wish we had all come together in that new gym, and we could have had somebody speaking, saying, "Close your eyes, if you will, and imagine a new Picher."

I wish we could have seen a new Picher in our mind's eye and worked backwards about how to achieve that. What do we need to have in place in six months, what in three years? In seven years? Is our goal to be totally gone or relocated somewhere else?

Our hearts are tied to Picher because it is our home with many memories, but our minds tell us that we must separate ourselves from our way of life to make it better for the next generation. I can't do anything about the possibility of not being able to raise my daughter here. But I can do something about having my grandchildren being raised here. That is all you can do. That is like Oprah says, When you know better, you do better.

John Mott

Oklahoma Water Resources Board OU1
Picher resident

John Mott displays the book given to him by the author, David Robertson for his assistance in providing background information.

I'm John Mott and I have lived in Picher all my life. I am 80 years old. My grandparents and my father came into Picher in 1917 with a wholesale house to sell groceries.

In 1925 there was a train wreck in Quapaw and my Dad went over there with his truck to see what he might find as salvage. He bought a whole carload of trees that were heading for Texas. They were silver leaf maple and catalpa trees. He sold those trees to all the grocery stores in town. You look at the pictures of Picher before 1925 and there was not a tree to be seen. Now you can look over the country and see thousands. That is because of my father.

My wife and I were both born in Picher and raised there. My wife and I got married in 1945, sixty-two years with the same woman. We raised a family there. I bought a house in 1950—of course it is being appraised and bought out. We lived there almost fifty-eight years. It is kind of hard to walk away from everything.

In 1980 the Oklahoma Water Resources Board came in and asked me to show them some things. I worked with them during what was later called OU1. I have always been an avid sportsman and ever ready to share what I have learned with anyone willing to listen.

I am patiently waiting to hear something so I can start all over again.

121

Small subsidence behind the
Picher Boys and Girls Club.

My family has been in Ottawa County for three generations.
I've been practicing family medicine here for twenty years.

Mark Osborn, MD
Family Physician
Lead Impacted Community
Relocation Trust

I become concerned about lead exposures in 1999 when I met Susan Waldron, and she got me involved with the Ottawa County Health Coalition, which was a multistakeholder group that was looking at ways to decrease lead levels in our children. Then I was on Governor Keating's Tar Creek Task Force and got involved in several other aspects, including the Health Effects Subcommittee, and subsequently, the Trust for the buy-out.

I am in support of the buy-out. It was necessary because the damage in Picher and Cardin was so severe that it wasn't a place where people should live. There were two major factors. One was the risk of elevated blood lead levels, and the second was the risk of subsidence or cave-in because of the hard rock mining underneath much of the community.

The EPA, unfortunately, does not have the statutory authority or ability to evaluate subsidence, and so the yard remediations and everything else they did had to be done without looking at that. When we finally were able to get the subsidence risk evaluated by the Army Corps of Engineers, it turns out that there are multiple areas, hundreds of areas, throughout the communities that have risk of significant subsidence, a risk of more than 20% over time of caving in, including six areas underneath Highway 69, the elementary school playground, the public park, you name it.

If you look at the map, it's like a piece of Swiss cheese. It's a public safety issue. And even though we've made great progress with the lead levels, it doesn't take away the risk to public safety of subsidence, and you just shouldn't allow people to live there. The other highway to town is even more undermined than Highway 69. There's no way to go anywhere in these towns without having to cross some area that's a risk for subsidence. So once we had that information, then it became obvious to Senator Inhofe and other people that it's not a place where people should live, and that's been the impetus behind proceeding with the buy-out.

I give Senator Inhofe and his staff a lot of credit. They worked very hard to get funding or approval for appropriations to finish the buy-out. It has been their number one priority. Inhofe has been in the senate for a long time, and this is a small area. It's not a lot of votes. But they believe it's the right thing to do, and they have taken it on wholeheartedly. Prior to the subsidence report, he was adamantly opposed to the buy-out, based upon the lead levels going down. What I admire about Senator Inhofe is that it takes a man of character to be able to reevaluate a situation and do something differently.

We need to treat the property owners fairly and get them good value for their property. People have had homes there for thirty or forty years, and as the march of knowledge has changed, their properties have become worthless, as worthless as if you built a dam and flooded them out.

You have to realize that the CDC lead level determinations have changed. So those people who lived there didn't even know they had a problem until the CDC had the knowledge base to realize that it was an issue. That's what I consider to be the march of knowledge.

We were all doing the best we could with what information we had, and as that information changed, we had to change what we thought should happen here.

Rob Weaver
Member of the Quapaw Tribe

I wanted to be the face that affects us.

A lot of the Quapaws feel beaten down. Their stories are not getting heard. I am tired of not getting the story out. It has to stop at some point. Every Indian has been cheated out of something. If you do your research, people who were sent in to protect us, the Bureau of Indian Affairs, didn't. This is not me coming up with this. This is fact. I just don't want this issue to go to the wayside. It took three generations before one person in my family would speak and I can only speak for the Quapaws. My grandfather, Arthur Buffalo, a fullblood Quapaw was born in 1890 and died in 1970 of tuberculosis. I have heard from my aunts and my uncles that he remembered what the land was supposed to look like before the mining, what this land was supposed to be. What is striking—I found a document that my grandfather signed with an "X" and I thought to myself, I wonder how well they described that document to him. Times have changed. Quapaw Indians no longer speak only our language. They are doctors, lawyers, they are engineers, they are businessmen, they are people who can change things. I just want to encourage every person to open your mind to the fact that things have to change and that we intend to do it.

When all the people get out of Cardin and Picher through the buy-out, I don't want you to forget a whole nation. A sovereign nation, a whole tribe, their land is completely devalued. Forty square miles cannot be fixed in day, even if they tried.

Everyone realizes that this is not going to be a habitable area for a long, long time, if ever, for humans. The reality is there could be other uses of the land, like a wildlife preserve, to carry on the traditions of the Quapaw people.

I, for one, as a Quapaw am no longer going to stand idly by. Our government officials: It is time for the greedy money that was made years ago from the land given to us to be paid to the people who have lived in near poverty for all these times. This is still affecting Quapaws. I hope that this issue is spread everywhere.

If the tribes don't stand up and stop this, then one day the tribes are going to die out. We are not going to remember the culture, we won't remember who we were or what we stood for, or our languages will die out because greed got in the way.

Tim Kent
Environmental Director
Quapaw Tribe

The tribe is going to be here forever.

Up until recently, it has been difficult to get the tribe's influence into the cleanup plan for the chat. John Berrey is the Chairman for the Quapaw Tribe. Because of his insistence and political contacts, we have been able to convince EPA to hire some really good scientists who have put together a tribal alternative that has been for the most part accepted by the EPA. We are excited about that.

The EPA's first proposal was to come in and cap and fence a bunch of chat piles, areas that the tribe would not be able to use. This is just another example of a taking from the tribe. There have been some pretty good developments since then. It hasn't been the same old, "The tribe gets the shaft in the end." The tribe has been driving the new aggressive proposal for cleanup, and it is being accepted, which is amazing.

The tribe's big thing was that the tribal people use the resources more than the general public, and cleaning it up to the acceptance of the general public is not acceptable to the tribe. Plus the tribe is going to be here forever. People may get bought out, but the tribe is going to be here because this is the only land the government gave the Quapaw to be Quapaw land. That has been the major sticking issue with the tribe and EPA. They have not been willing to clean up to background conditions, which is the level that would truly protect the tribe. What EPA is going to do now may get us to background, but they are not committing to background. If they are going to scrape up all the chat and take it away, we will be back to the pre-mine era, and that will be protective of the tribe. We have been asking for them to put that in their Record of Decision and commit to background conditions. In the final analysis, what they do may get us there.

If that is the only sticking issue left, it's not totally a deal breaker. Frankly, if they do leave some chat, that leaves room for Natural Resource Damage Assessment (NRDA) to come in, which can bridge the gap between cleanup and total restoration. The tribe can go after that.

Lessons Learned....

There are three components to consider about these sites: politics, science, and policy. You have to have all three present. One without the other two doesn't get it. If you have politics and the policy without the science, you are not going to get it done.

The science costs money. EPA has committed to giving a certain amount of money to hire scientists who can get the data. The only way to get the money it takes to get it done is to stomp your feet. Tell your senator, the tribe says, "We are getting the shaft." So your senator has to make a call to EPA saying that they should give the tribe some resources so they can have a seat at the table. EPA can give you a seat at the table, but it may be just so they can say, "We had them at the table." But if you have the tribe and their scientist at the table giving hard scientific facts, they can't refute or ignore you. Then you have a real seat at the table. They have to listen to you then because you can prove to them on paper that your concerns are legitimate. It takes that.

You can't have just a tribal member or even the Environmental Director deal with the government. You have to have someone with clout and some expertise, with qualifications and experience in dealing with this type of situation. It is just like having a lawyer—you have to have a scientist here, talking scientific language for you. Until you have that, EPA can just frankly ignore you, but they can't ignore the scientific facts. You get the money to get the data to back you up. That is what it takes: politics, science and getting the public behind you. Then you can start to be noticed. EPA has a tribal policy that they have to consult with tribes, and a lot of them just go through the motions. They have no intention of changing their view on how they think the site is going. If they get physically stopped with the scientists and the politicians, they have to stop and pay attention to you. Then you have something. That has been the case here, and I am sure that other tribes can relate to that.

The EPA gives tribes money to start environmental programs, but, quite frankly, the environmental directors who work for tribes don't have the funding or the time to do something like this. It takes a big effort and bigger science. EPA doesn't give you the funding to attract nationally known scientists that you need to get the data and the facts straight.

It has taken two years to get from the first plan to the second. It took John Berrey going to Congress to stop the first process, and the State of Oklahoma has been right with us. What is the first process? We have been able to get EPA on board with consolidating all of the chat in one place, getting rid of all the chat and getting it down to virgin soil. We don't want to have fenced, capped areas that you can't use. That is the best plan, and they are getting ready to bring it out to the public. It would be economically feasible to consolidate all the chat and sell it. Chat sellers are not going to go out to a chat base and scrape up the last three to four feet because it is not worth it to them. Why spend the money to

cap and fence it when it saves money to take the chat to someone who is selling it? These common sense approaches that we have been able to slip into the cleanup plan are going to make a huge difference in reclaiming that land out there.

Just like anything else,
making big changes takes money,
and EPA has less money every year.
You have to be the squeaky wheel,
but you cannot be as squeaky
as your senator can be.
That is what it takes.
It's worked for us.

Photo by Tina Smith

Just because the buy-out is going on does not mean that the problem is over. It means it is just beginning.

John Berrey
Chairman of the Quapaw Tribe

We live Tar Creek, even though I live in Osage County. I sent a letter to EPA today and said if you drive through Picher and down Douthit road, nothing has changed. Nothing has really changed since they put us on the National Priorities List thirty years ago. This is a disgrace, and it is sad.

Millions and millions of dollars and thousands of hours later show EPA's OU1's berms sitting in a pond; they were supposed to protect the ground water. EPA is finishing up replacing yards of abandoned houses, while relocation people negotiate with the owner on buying them out. But no one has done anything about the water, the air, and the aquifer that is the drinking water source. Nothing is being done about it. We are sick and tired of that. I am a Republican, and I am ashamed of our federal government. Most Indian people are patriotic. Think about all the Indian guys in the war. I am ashamed right now of the EPA, the BIA, and the Department of the Interior because they have spent all this time, but if you drive through Picher and down Douthit road, it still looks the same. No one cares about the people who live here.

So the Quapaw Tribe has decided to step up. For the past ten years, we have been asked if we wanted to stay our case. This time we said, "No, we don't want to stay our case anymore. We want to find a judge and jury to hear our case about how the mining companies and railroads and the Department of the Interior destroyed our earth, our food, our water, and they don't care."

We have decided to go after them full tilt. We have spent several million dollars of our money preparing for litigation to sue the mining companies, to sue the BIA, and to sue the railroad companies. What does that mean to us in the community? It means using the CERCLA law to sue the principally responsible parties for restoration. Under the law, any money we receive must be spent on reclamation and fixing the problem. It is not the kind of case where the Quapaw Tribe will receive money and run. The Quapaw Tribe has no where else to go. In the 1830s they sent us here from Arkansas and drew a line on a map, and we could only be Quapaw inside that line.

We are going to stay here. We are going to stay here with the other tribes. They have the same problem. They can't go anywhere else and be who they are. This is the only place we are recognized legally. Our hope is that we will be able to show that the mining companies knew that they were destroying the earth and destroying the water, destroying the fish, destroying the plants, and destroying everything while they were doing it. They were not surprised. They knew the whole time they were doing it that the land and water would be ruined, and we are going to prove it.

We don't want EPA or BIA to fix it. We want to fix it. Not just the Quapaw Tribe, we want the people of Ottawa County to fix it. If we don't fix it, then in twenty, thirty, forty, maybe eighty years, we won't be able to drink water from the Roubidoux aquifer. Without water we won't have anything. People who are head of the BIA have been invited to come but now will not respond to letters. They say what they think you want to hear while you are standing in front of them, but as soon as you walk away, they turn their backs on you. What they are doing now is not preparing as trustees, as they are supposed to be. They are hunkering down in their offices and figuring out how to protect themselves from being sued. They have a hundred years of screwing up that they can't run and hide from.

We are tired of giving Tar Creek Toxic Tour trips with dignitaries and hearing them say, "We feel for you. We are going to fix it." Then they walk away and leave us. We want to change the dynamic, and the only way we know how right now is by asking to take action and suing them in front of a federal judge. We believe we will be successful because if you drive through Picher or go down Douthitt road, it is pretty obvious that there are problems. If you listen to scientists who are at the Tar Creek conferences, it is pretty obvious that there are problems. Someone is responsible for these problems, and these people, like the mining companies, stole millions of dollars and took it to other towns and cities and didn't leave any of it here. We have appealed to BIA, to the state, and to everybody who will listen to us. The Quapaw Tribe wants that land that is being bought out. We don't want to build houses or casinos on the land. What we want to do is use the land to fix the problem. We want to turn to science that is outside the federal government to partner with us to solve our ground water problems and to use the chat in environmentally sensible ways in asphalt.

I drove up on the turnpike today. They need asphalt to fix all the holes. We want to keep pushing forward looking for ways to transport chat without causing problems. The EPA and the BIA want to build a big fence around that land, tell scientists to stay out, and they want to then cover everything with clay. That doesn't do anything for the ground water, the surface water, or the Roubidoux aquifer. That doesn't do anything for the health of the people in Ottawa County.

We don't want them to do that. We want them to remove the chat, and we want to turn to hydrologists who understand ground water and mine cavities and streams that are dumping thousands of pounds of heavy metals in the creek. We want to take that land back.

People view the Quapaw tribe in different ways. I see the Quapaw Tribe as struggling to find our place in this crazy life. We thought the BIA and EPA were actually here to help protect us. We always trusted them. We have gotten to the time that we don't want to trust them anymore.

Thankfully because of the buy-out those people will finally get a fair deal for their homes, and with them out of the way, we can get underway, with the goal of helping everybody—everybody in Ottawa County, everyone swimming in Grand Lake or anyone getting water out of the Roubidoux aquifer.

We are serious; we are going to war. Indians like to fight; we fight each other all the time. We are pretty excited about fighting someone else for awhile. Stay tuned.

The Quapaw Tribe wants to see it cleaned up.

Looking to the Future

Here are some thoughts about what can or might come next from some of the people who have told their stories here. Many possibilities and much work lie ahead; that much is certain, both for the Tar Creek community and for others.

Tami McKeon

There is something even better than the lead-based-paint programs available now. HUD has a program for healthy homes. It allows LPB abatement along with more cost-effective reduction measures, rather than strict abatement alone. They want to test for mold, radon, pesticides and other environmental hazards that might occur within a home. So you can have a total effect, not just putting people in programs for just this or that.

A community or non-profit organization must apply for the Healthy Homes. I don't know if anyone has applied for it. I think that would be a really great thing to let communities know about this opportunity. The Home Builders Association is really stressing green building. They all go hand in hand,

setting parameters for having healthy, safe, decent, sanitary homes for every income sector. When all that's in place, then we will know that at least our homes, schools, and daycares are not making our children sick.

Susan Waldron

The blood lead levels coming down is a piece of the success. There's still many tons of chat still above the ground. There's still pollution in the air. Cleanup's not finished. People who want to relocate are not relocated. Issues are not all resolved, and will they be able to be resolved in a person's lifetime? I don't know. Will there ever be enough money to resolve everything? Will people be satisfied? I don't know.

ATSDR

Challenge for the future—Ensure that neighborhoods surrounding Superfund sites become healthy places. All of the work we do is geared toward meeting the overarching goal of ensuring that the sites where we work become healthy places to live, work and play.

Mark Osborn

To me, once you move the people out of Picher and Cardin, the process of moving the chat becomes less important and the process of protecting the watershed becomes more important, limiting the damage to the surrounding area by not having runoff from chat piles and from the mine ponds contaminating Tar Creek, which then contaminates Neosho River, which then contaminates Grand Lake. I hope the EPA will aggressively pursue watershed work, as opposed to spending a lot of money on moving chat once the people are gone, because we'll have plenty of time to do that.

We need topsoil on the remaining chat to markedly limit any exposure. If we can get it covered and get the streambeds so they don't go across bare dust and through the mine ponds, I think we can take care of 95% or 98% of the source of exposure. The sixty-four-million-dollar question is: if we buy all these people out, what are we going to do with the area? What do we want it to become and how do we make sure that it can't ever be used for people to build homes on again? I hope that the solution will be scientifically driven by what limits exposure and what limits transfer to the rest of the watershed.

Earl Hatley

The EPA is getting started on what they call OU4, to cap the remaining mineshafts, remove the chat piles, scrape the ground and plant native grasses. Parallel with OU4 is OU5, a unique situation in the country since it is one of the first sites where two EPA regions, three states, ten Indian tribes and a citizens group (LEAD Agency) are involved in one operable unit called Universal Operable Unit 5. The Army Corps of Engineers did a lot of the scoping and preliminary investigation, bringing all the stakeholders together and actually laying out the details of what would need to be done, the stages of total cleanup, for the tri-state mining district and its downstream impacts. They prioritized what needs to be done first and laid out a time line. That became the basis of OU5.

It's also called the Spring River Watershed but it is going to include Tar Creek and the Neosho River from Tar Creek to Grand Lake. They are starting at the headwaters of Spring River in Missouri where the acid mine water and the chat runoff first hit the tributaries that run into the river. They are going to stop the bleeding there and then come down the streams. The gravel bars in those streams are chat bars. They are going to come in and scoop out the gravel bars and wait a few years. The bars will probably reappear. Over time as they reappear, they are going to scoop them out until it is natural, it is not chat.

They'll work their way all the way down to Twin Bridges. It is anticipated that by the time they get to Twin Bridges, the berms and all the channelization and remediation planned for the channel of Tar Creek will have been completed. So there will be no more pollution coming from the Tar Creek site. Then they can proceed from Twin Bridges on down to Grand Lake, which they really don't have a plan for yet.

I am hoping that by the time OU4 is completed twenty years from now, OU5 will already be finished. So by the time they put the finishing touches by planting the seeds on the remediated Tar Creek site, Grand Lake will be dealt with, the fish will be edible again, and everything will be the way it should be. Then we can have that fish tournament. Actually we can have the tournament sooner. Once the bleeding stops and all that clears out, there is no reason why Tar Creek couldn't have fish again, and that won't take twenty years. That won't take five years. If they get with it. If they get with it.

Robert O. Wright, MD
Harvard School of Public Health

This community is succeeding and this is important for other communities to know because they found a way to overcome group inertia. It is very difficult to both believe that you can make change occur and then determine the means to make that change. Inertia is the natural state. Most folks accept what is going on around them, even if there is unfairness or injustice. This community decided not to passively accept their children's high blood lead levels.

I believe that partnerships developed (whether planned or by accident) whereby advocacy groups like LEAD made the public aware of the problem, a strong proactive health department found lead poisoned children and intervened on their behalf. I believe work of state and federal agencies in publicizing the problem and conducting clean up in the area all played a role. TEAL was clearly important and the tribes clearly made sure that the environmental issues were always up for discussion and never brushed under the table. Silence is the best friend of inertia.

It's not over. As long as there is lead in chat piles and chat piles exist, the problem could come back.

Piles of mine tailings, locally called "chat" are used as a source for gravel and as seen in this photo, for recreation.

Photographers

The Tar Creek Superfund Site is a visual disaster. Images provided by the following photographers have shown the environment—the acid mine water, the chat mountains, sink holes, sometimes used for swimming, and even the very dust in the air. Their work has powerfully covered the plight of this land. Many of the photographs in this book come from their archives and were selected to help tell this story.

Earl Dotter

What impressed me most while spending time photographing in Tar Creek was the mountainous scale of the environmental concerns in relation to the impacted communities. It is not often that the visual manifestations of an environmental problem loom as large as they do here in this Superfund site, home to so many Native Americans.

I feel we are succeeding well with photos of the environmental damage, but we are far less successful in showing the health consequences of lead exposure.

Tina Smith

I was delighted to be chosen as principal photographer for this project. I learned so many things about the community I grew up in and the dangers never brought to my attention. Having two small children of my own, I wanted to learn more so I could keep them safe. With so many obvious dangers lurking around every corner, I never considered the environment, like the water in strip pits or sink holes that looks so beautiful and inviting with high levels of lead as well as the airborne toxins via the chat piles.

I was stunned and appalled that more has not been done to fix this mess created so long ago. The mess left over from the mines has been there all my life and it just became something of an oddity to see when passing through. I hope that others can become informed on how to keep their families safe and that devastation caused to the area, the creeks and wildlife, can be restored during my life.

Nancy Goldenberg

I was introduced to the Tar Creek area long before my first impressions developed of what a landscape should be. My family moved to Oklahoma in the early 1970s, and our first drive through Picher and the impressive piles of chat lining the highway proved thrilling. There were motorcycles criss-crossing the hills, hang-gliders launching from the pile's peaks and, in the winter, sleds careening down the slopes. It appeared to be a wonderland of fun and excitement, and, in my young imagination, only the Rocky Mountains equaled its majesty. This stark contrast to what my twelve-year-old self believed the landscape of the Great Plains should be created a sense of wonder and fascination.

A quarter of a century later, this interest led to an intense desire to document this landscape through photographs and record its ever-changing nature. I might have taken the landscape's uniqueness for granted had I grown up in the area. That relatively late, yet impressionable, introduction left the desire to learn more. It gave me the advantage of a lasting interest and the basis to create The Tar Creek Series, a sequence of photographs depicting the effects of mining on the landscape.

Despite the potential dangers, the Tar Creek site also has a youthful nostalgia and a feeling of home for me. It was impossible for me to dismiss the beauty. It will be interesting to see the Tar Creek site in twenty-five years, to wonder about our successes—and perhaps failures, but always while contemplating the beauty of home.

Vaughn Wascovich

I am a fine-art photographer currently teaching at Texas A&M University in Commerce, Texas. I have also held the appointment of Visiting Scholar with the Harvard School of Public Health since 2004. My photographic research interests have always been concerned with issues of the land and man's relationship to the physical environment.

I became aware of the Tar Creek Superfund Site when Nancy Goldenberg, then a photography student from Columbia College Chicago, first showed me images from this incredible site. When I moved to Missouri in 2001 to teach at the University of Missouri, I took a drive to northeast Oklahoma to see the region in person. What I saw amazed and saddened and scared me.

One hot summer day I was sitting in the small Picher bar. The bartender asked me what I was doing in this little town, and when I told her that I was photographing the area, she said, "Please don't make our town look ugly. There are times, when the snow is covering the chat piles, that this is one of the most beautiful places on earth." From that one conversation I came to understand that I should try to document both the current environmental problems found at Tar Creek and the people's close relationship to this land, and in spite of the obvious hazards, their reluctance to leave.

Glossary of Terms and Abbreviations

ATSDR   Agency for Toxic Substances and Disease Registry; a part of the U.S. Department of Health and Human Services

BLL   blood lead level

CAB   Community Advisory Board, the initial community group formed for the TEAL project

CERCLA   Comprehensive Environmental Response Compensation and Liability Act; The 1980 act of congress that established the Superfund tax program for the purpose of cleaning up abandoned or uncontrolled hazardous waste sites

CHAMP   Community Health Action Monitoring Program; a program funded by mining companies to determine sources of lead poisoning in the Tar Creek Superfund site

CVS   Cherokee Volunteer Society

EPA   Environmental Protection Agency; a U.S. federal agency

HUD   U.S. Department of Housing and Urban Development

LICRT   Lead Impacted Community Relocation Trust
The name given to the monies allocated for relocating families at highest risk of lead poisoning in the mining towns of Picher and Cardin

MOU   Memorandum of Understanding; a legal document describing agreed-upon roles and responsibilities

NEAHEC   Northeast Area Health Education Center; a state and federally funded agency with a mission to alleviate health care shortages in the rural and urban underserved areas; allied with several colleges and hospitals, mainly in Kentucky, its main office is located in Morehead, KY

NIEHS   National Institute of Environmental Health Sciences; one of the National Institutes of Health within the U.S. Department of Health and Human Services; the NIEHS campus is located in Research Triangle Park, NC

OEH   Occupational and Environmental Health

ORU   Oral Roberts University

OSDH   Oklahoma State Department of Health

OSUCHS   Oklahoma State University Center for Health Sciences

OU1 (2, 3)   Operable Unit 1 (etc.); EPA designations for individual work projects

QUAPAW   Quapaw Unites Against Pollution and Waste; the name of the Quapaw student group

ROD   Record of Decision; an EPA public document that explains which cleanup alternatives will be used to clean up a Superfund site

NPL   National Priorities List; an EPA list of the most hazardous areas in the country, listed in order of highest risk

NRDA   Natural Resource Damage Assessment; a process to identify the extent of resource injuries and the best methods to restore those resources

SEAL   Student Efforts Against Lead; the name of the Picher–Cardin student group

TEAL   Tribal Efforts Against Lead; the name chosen for the project to gather blood lead levels in children and to educate the community about lead-poisoning prevention measures

Bibliography

After 19 years, nation's number one superfund site still not cleaned up. 2002, September. *Leaving Our Communities at Risk*, 33-36. San Francisco, CA: Sierra Club.

Bland A. D., M. C. Kegler, C. Escoffery, and L. Halinka Malcoe. 2005, July. Understanding childhood lead poisoning preventive behaviors: the roles of self-efficacy, subjective norms, and perceived benefits. *Preventive Medicine* 41: 70-78.

Blowing in the wind: The lessons of Tar Creek. (2003, Fall). *OSU Physician* 8(1): 5-7.

Caron, J. 2003, October. Lessons from a wounded place. *Friends Bulletin* 74(8): 14-16.

Caron, J. 2004, November 2. Biology and "The Bomb." *Engineering & Science* 67(2): 16-27.

Cherokee Volunteer Society. 2002. *Tar Creek anthology 2: Our toxic place*. Los Angeles, CA: ABCD Books.

Concerned Youth and Citizens, Miami, Oklahoma. 1999. *Tar Creek anthology: The legacy*. Tahlequah, OK: Tahlequah Daily Press.

Horton, M. 1998. *The long haul: An autobiography*. New York: Teachers College Press.

Hu, H., J. Shine, and R. O Wright. 2007. The challenge posed to children's health by mixtures of toxic waste: The Tar Creek Superfund Site as a case study. *Pediatr Clin N Am,* 54: 155-175.

Kegler, M. C., and L. H. Malcoe. 2004, October. Results from a lay health advisor intervention to prevent lead poisoning among rural Native American children. *Am J of Public Health*, 94: 1730-1735.

Kegler, M. C.; L. H. Malcoe, R. A. Lynch, and S. Whitecrow-Ollis. 2000. A community-based intervention to reduce lead exposure among Native American children. *Environ Epid and Tox* 2: 121-132.

Kegler, M. C., L. H. Malcoe, R. Scott, R. A. Lynch, and R. Tolliver. 1999. Caregiver beliefs and behaviors in the prevention of childhood lead poisoning. *Fam and Com Health*, 22(1): 50-65.

Kegler, M. C., R. Stern, S. Whitecrow-Ollis, and L. H. Malcoe. 2003, April. Assessing lay health advisor activity in an intervention to prevent lead poisoning in Native American children. *Health Prom Prac* 4(2): 189-196.

Kesson, K., and C. Oyler. 1992, January. Integrated curriculum and service learning: Linking school-based knowledge and social action. *English Education* 31(2). Available at www.ncte.org

Kim, R. 1995, October 21. Childhood lead linked to adult obesity. *Science News* 148(17): 268.

Lindley, T. 1999, December 9. Who will save the children of Ottawa County? *The Oklahoman*, A1.

Lindley, T. 1999, December 10. Another broken promise. *The Oklahoman*, A1.

Lindley, T. 1999, December 11. Scars of lead poisoning. *The Oklahoman*, A1.

Lindley, T. 1999, December 17. Miami mayor asks for limits on chat. *The Oklahoman*, A1.

Lynch, R. A., L. H. Malcoe, V. J. Skaggs, and M. C. Kegler. 2000, October. The relationship between residential lead exposures and elevated blood lead levels in a rural mining community. *Environ Health*: 9-15.

Malcoe, L. H., R. A. Lynch, M. C. Kegler, and V. J. Skaggs. 2002, April. Lead sources, behaviors, and socioeconomic factors in relation to blood lead of Native American and white children: A community-based assessment of a former mining area. *Environ Health Pers* 110, Suppl 2: Community, Research, and Environmental Justice: 221-231.

Roosevelt, M. 2004, April 26. The tragedy of Tar Creek. *Time*: 42-44, 47.

Singer, H. H., and M. C. Kegler. 2004, December. Assessing interorganizational networks as a dimension of community capacity: Illustrations from a community intervention to prevent lead poisoning. *Health, Education and Behavior* 31(6): 808-821.

Wright R. O, C. Amarasiriwardena, A. D. Woolf, R. Jim, and D. C. Bellinger. 2006. Neuropsychological correlates of hair arsenic, manganese, and cadmium levels in school-age children residing near a hazardous waste site. *Neurotoxicology*, 27: 210-216.

Recommended Reading

Brugge, D., T. Benally, and E. Yazzie-Lewis. 2006. *The Navajo people and uranium mining*. Albuquerque: University of New Mexico Press.

Chavis, Jr., B. F., and C. Lee. 1987. *Toxic wastes and race in the United States: A national report on the racial and socio-economic characteristics of communities with hazardous waste sites*. Cleveland, OH: United Church of Christ, Commission for Racial Justice.

Davis, D. 2002. *When smoke ran like water: Tales of environmental deception and the battle against pollution*. New York: Basic Books.

Dotter, E. 1998. *The quiet sickness: A photographic chronicle of hazardous work in America*. Fairfax, VA: American Industrial Hygiene Association.

Hatley, E. 2007. Tar Creek Superfund Site. In *Grandmother Tears, Mother Earth mines: Mineral extraction on indigenous lands in the U.S.* by Indigenous Environmental Network, 58-59. Bemidji, MN: Author.

Hawken, P. 2007. *Blessed unrest*. New York: Penguin.

Kaye, C. B. 2004. *The complete guide to service learning: Proven, practical ways to engage students in civic responsibility, academic curriculum, & social action*. Los Angeles, CA: Free Spirit.

Kennedy, R. F., Jr. 2004. *Crimes against nature*. New York: HarperCollins.

Louv, R. 2006. *Last child in the woods: Saving our children from nature-deficit disorder*. Chapel Hill, NC: Algonquin.

Markowitz, G. and D. Rosner. 200. *Deceit and denial: The deadly politics of industrial pollution*. Berkeley: University of California Press.

Navajo Uranium Miner Oral History and Photography Project. 1997. *Memories come to us in the rain and the wind*. Boston: Author and Tufts School of Medicine.

Robertson, D. 2006. *Hard as the rock itself: Place and identity in the American mining town.* Boulder: University of Colorado Press.

Scott, M. P. 2007. *Spirit of harmony* [songbook]. Santa Barbara, CA: Gesundheit Music.

Silko, L. M. 1977. *Ceremony.* New York: Penguin.

Toxic Wastes and Race at Twenty Years: 1987-2007. 2007, March. Cleveland, OH: United Church of Christ, Justice and Witness Ministries.

About the Editors

Rebecca Jim has been an innovative and relentless advocate for the health of Tar Creek residents since her arrival. She was the founder, guide and faculty adviser of the Cherokee Volunteer Society at Miami High School, Miami, Oklahoma, while she was the counselor there. She is a founding member and executive director of LEAD Agency, Inc.

Marilyn Power Scott is a freelance editor who lives in Santa Barbara, California. She first became aware of Tar Creek through Jennifer Caron and became involved when helping Rebecca Jim compile and edit the Cherokee Volunteer Society's *Tar Creek Anthology 2: Our Toxic Place*. She is honored to be part of the unfolding Tar Creek story.

Sinkholes on the west side of Commerce

Photo by Vaughn Wascovich

Photo by Vaughn Wascovich

Photo by Vaughn Wascovich